Here I Come!

Write the words. Stick the stickers.
Match the pictures to the words.

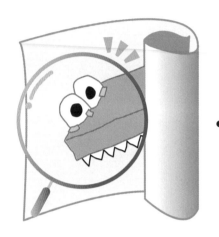

"Here I come!"
said the crocodile.

"Here I come!"
said the snake.

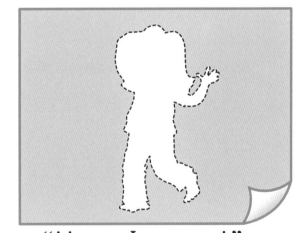

"Here I come!"
said the girl.

4

Read *Here I Come!* Help the girl get to Dad. Write the word. Say the words.

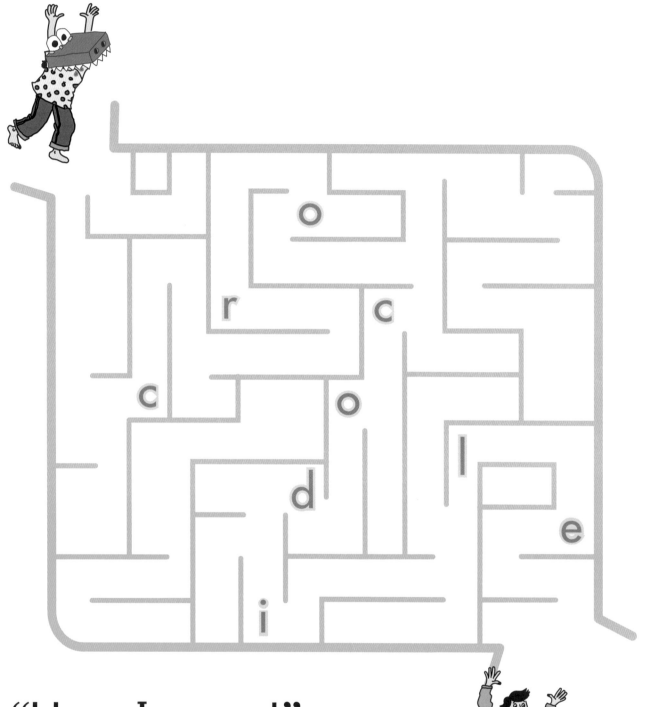

"Here I come!"
said the crocodile.

Here I go!

 Draw a monster. Write the words.
Say the words.

"H_____ I c_____!"
s_____ the m_____.

come   Here   monster   said

Join the dots to finish the picture.
Color the picture.
Write the word. Say the words.

"Here I come!" said the monster.

 Write the names of the animals.
Say the words. Use the Word Bank.

_____

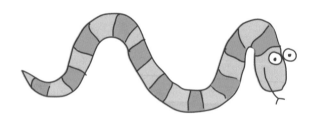

_____

shark
crocodile
tiger
snake

8

 Write the words. Say the words. Use the Word Bank.

Here I come!

A cr_____

Here I come!

A t_____

Here I come!

A m_____

Here I go!

tiger
crocodile
monster

9

Play the game.

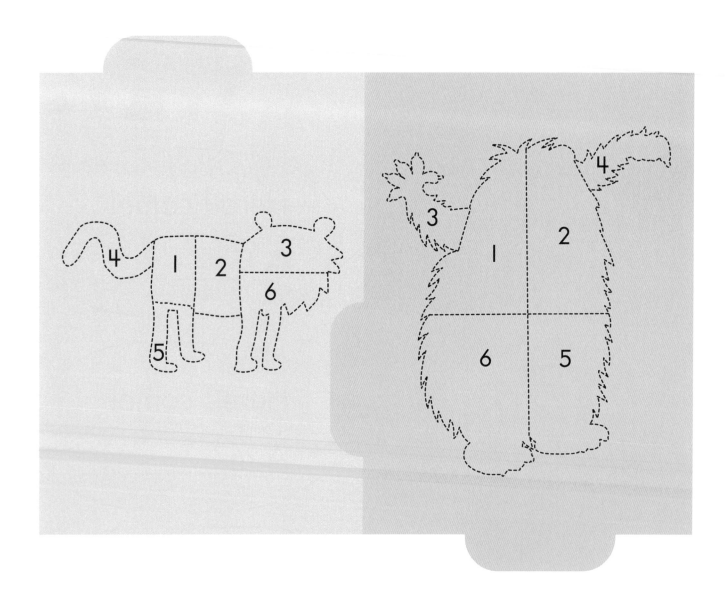

You need: number cube, stickers

1. Decide who goes first.
2. Choose your animal.
3. Throw the number cube. Stick the sticker in the space with the number on it.
4. The first player to cover the whole animal is the winner.

10

Stick the stickers to finish the pictures.
Match the pictures to the words.
Say the words.

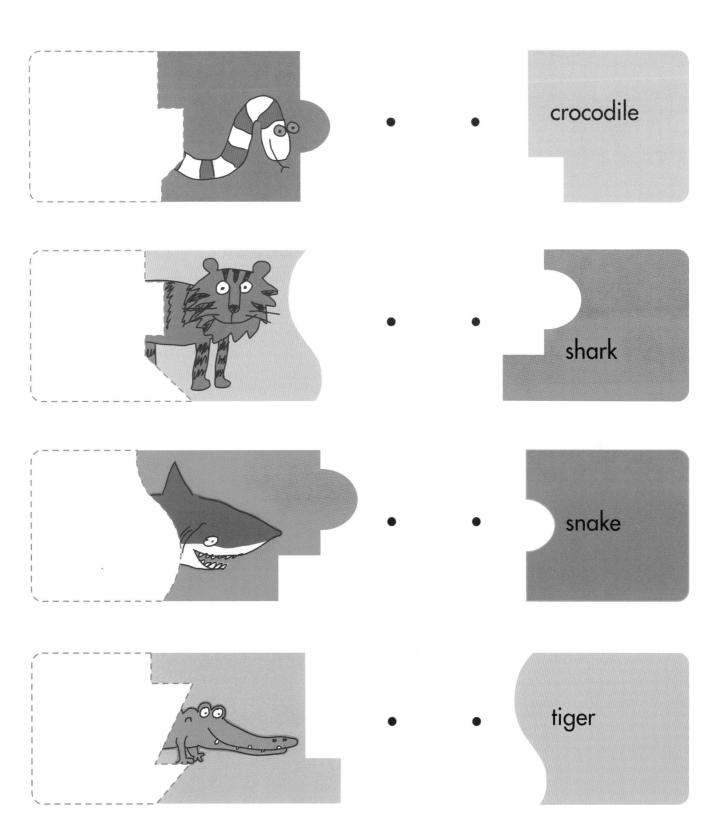

crocodile

shark

snake

tiger

11

Sticker Sheet 1

Write the words. Say the words.

"Here I go!"
said Dad.

Up and Down

Read *Up and Down*. Write the labels.
Use the Word Bank.

My ball

My pl_____

my cat

plane
kite
cat
balloon
my
ball

My _____

M_ b_____

14

Stick the stickers in the correct position.
Write up or down. Say the words.

My ball goes down.   My kite goes up.

My plane goes up.   My ball goes up.

My kite goes down.   My plane goes down.

15

Sticker Sheet 3

Do they go up or down? Stick the word stickers.

Stick the stickers to finish the words. Say the words.
Match the words to the pictures.
Practice writing the letter b, k, and p.

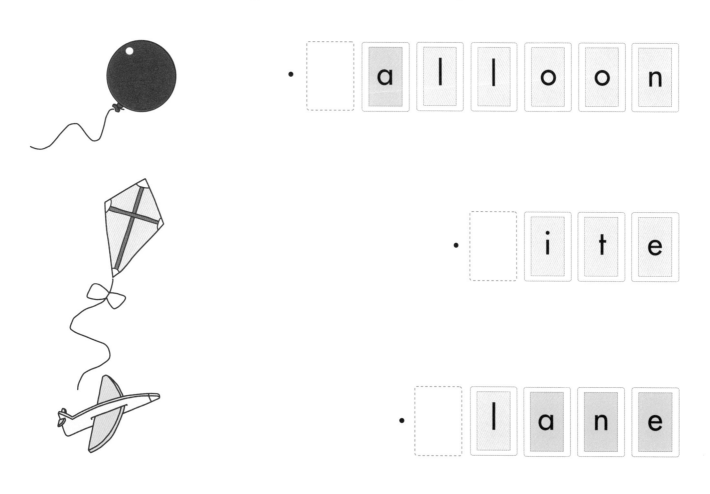

· a l l o o n

· i t e

· l a n e

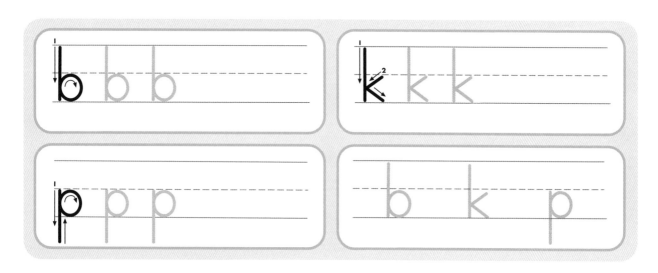

17

Sticker Sheet 3

Stick the stickers.
Match the pictures to words. Say the words.

up

down

My ball goes up.

My ball goes down.

My kite goes up.

My kite goes down.

My balloon goes up and up and up.

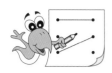

Match the letters and pictures with the words.
Say the words. Practice the letters f, v, h, g, and d.

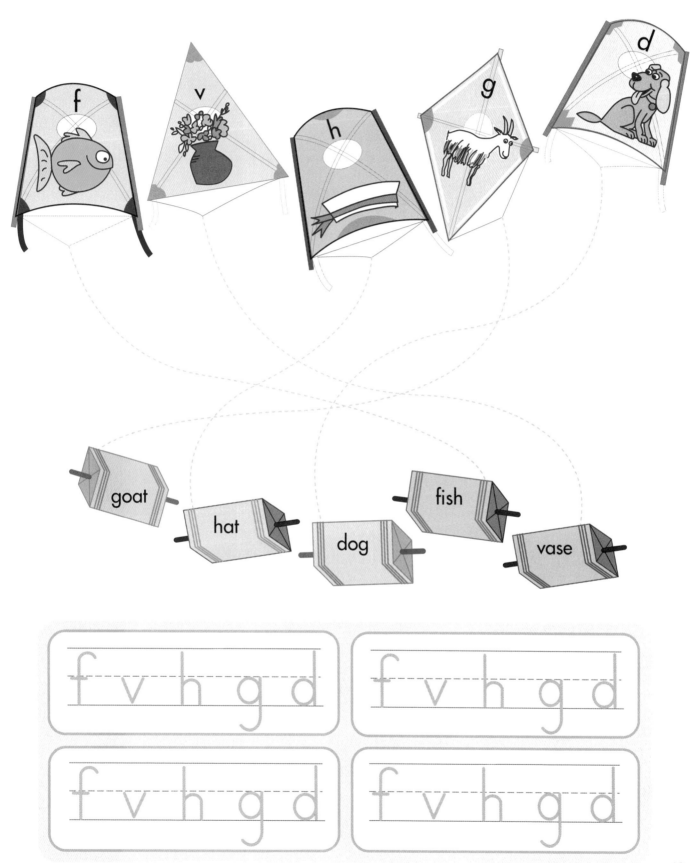

Use the coordinate grid. Find the letters on the chart.
Write the letters to finish the words.
Say the words.

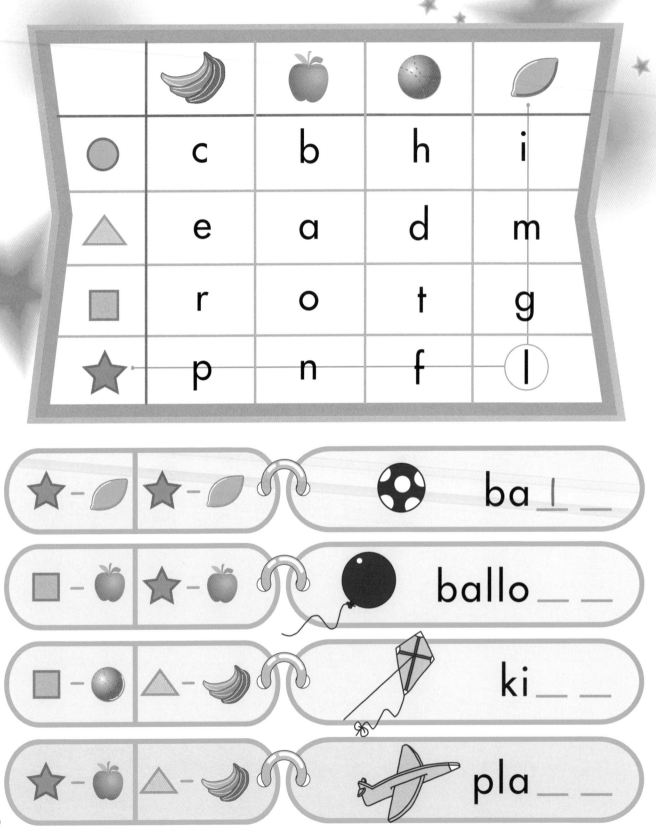

20

 Fill in the chart. Use the Word Bank.

What goes up?   What goes down?

My _____ 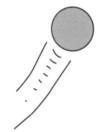   My _____

My _____ 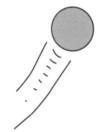   My _____

My _____   My _____

My _____

plane
kite
balloon
ball

21

 Write the words to make the sentences.

 My plane goes up.

My plane goes down.

 My kite goes up.

My kite goes down.

 My balloon goes up.

My balloon goes down.

Read *Water Fun*. Match the pictures and say the words.

I get my snorkel.   I get my mask.   I get my flippers.

24

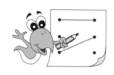 Match the words and pictures.
Say the words.

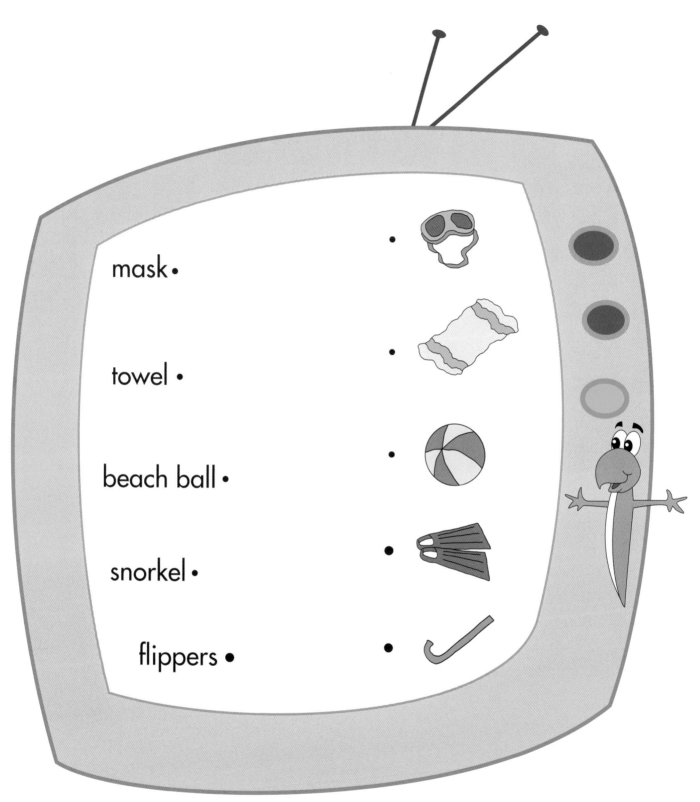

mask •

towel •

beach ball •

snorkel •

flippers •

25

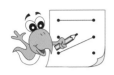

Find the water toys in the picture.
Match the toys to the words.

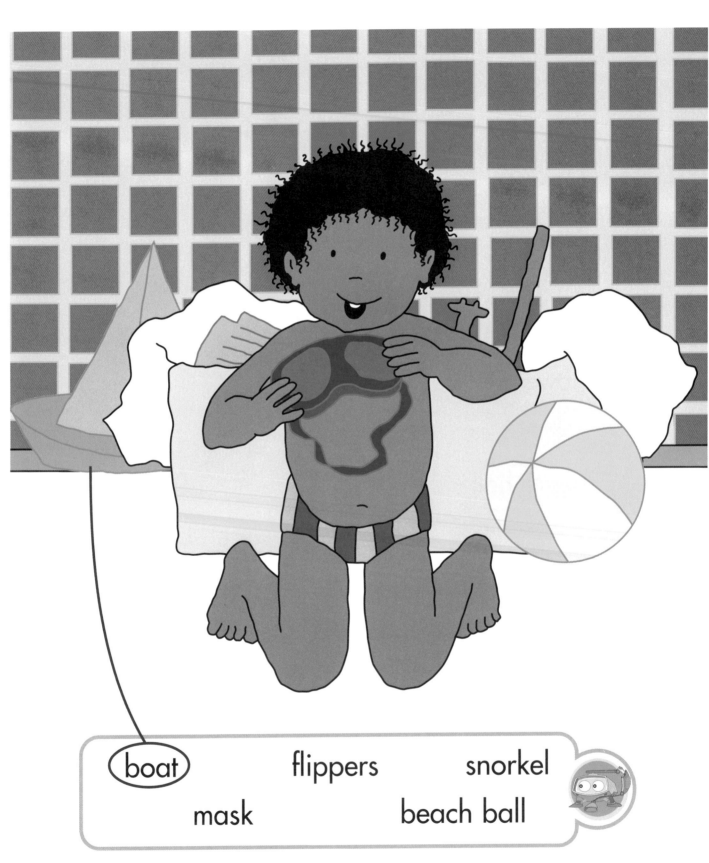

boat   flippers   snorkel

mask   beach ball

 Stick the stickers. Say the words.
Write the letters.

ask

oat

orkel ✓

ippers

owel

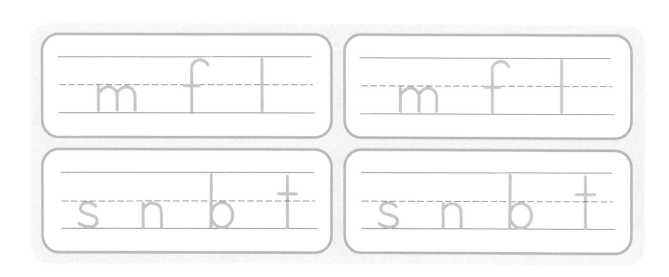

m f t

m f t

s n b t

s n b t

Sticker Sheet 2

Stick the stickers on the picture.
Write the words.

I love my bath.

Circle the things that begin with b.
Practice writing the letter b.

bath   ball   boat   boy

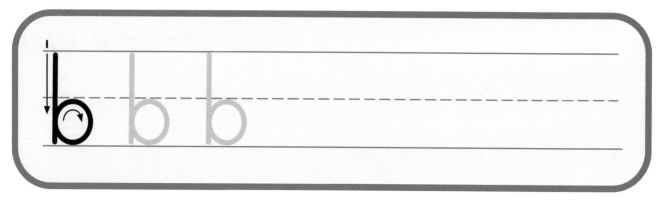

b   b   b

Play the game.

Start →

Finish

You need: counters, number cube

1. Decide who goes first.
2. Put your counters on **Start**.
3. Throw the number cube. If you get 1, 2, or 5 you can move 1, 2, or 5 spaces.
   Say, "I like…" Miss a turn if you get 3, 4, or 6.
4. The first player to reach **Finish** is the winner.

30

What is missing?
Stick the sticker to make the pages match.

flippers

mask

boat

towel

mask

boat

snorkel

towel

towel

boat

snorkel

flippers

snorkel

towel

mask

flippers

Sticker Sheet 2

 Write the words to make the sentences.

 I get my mask.

 I get my snorkel.

 I get my flippers.

 I get my beach ball

 I get my boat.

32 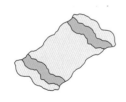 I get my towel.

I Can

Stick the stickers. Match the numbers and words. Say the words.

 Read *I Can*. Write the word. Draw the face to match. Read the words.

I can frown.

I can smile.

Stick the stickers. Say the words.
Practice writing the letters u, e, and i.

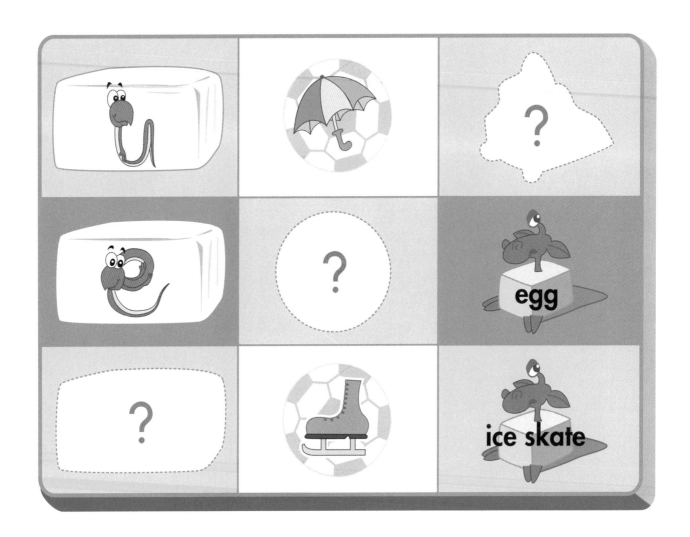

ŭ u u   ĕ e e

i i i   u e i

Find the path through the maze.
Stick the stickers on the numbers below.

Sticker Sheet 5

 Say the names of the shapes and color them in.
Write the word.

He can smile.

triangle   circle   rectangle   square

What letter does the word begin with?
Match the letter to the word. Write the letter.
Practice writing the letters q and v.

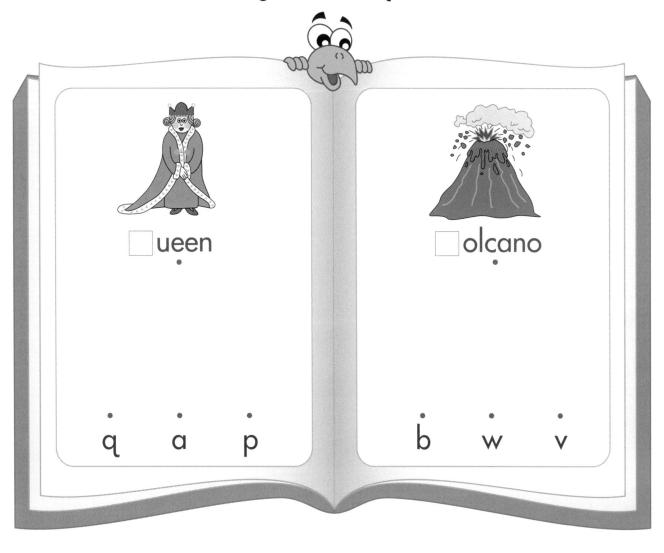

☐ueen

☐olcano

q · a · p ·

b · w · v ·

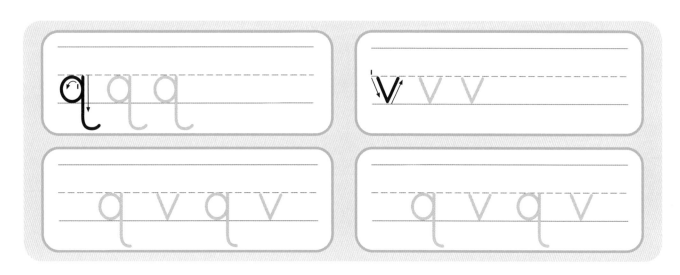

q q q

v v v

q v q v

q v q v

39

Play the game.

jump	jump	go	walk upside down	walk upside down
jump	jump	go	walk upside down	walk upside down
walk upside down	walk upside down	**start**	hop	hop
hop	hop	jump	go	go
hop	hop	jump	go	go

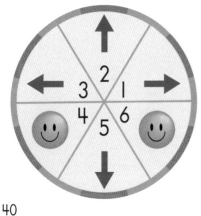

You need: counters, number cube
1. Make counters by sticking the stickers together.
   Choose the puppy or the girl. Decide who goes first.
2. Throw the number cube. Move only one space in the direction
   of the arrow. If you get 2, you move up the board.
   Say, "I can .." If you get a 4 or a 6, you can move in any direction.
3. The first player to reach a picture is the winner.

40

© 2006 Wendy Pye Publishing Ltd

What can the girl do? Stick the stickers.
Say the words. Circle the smile if the girl can do it.
Circle the frown if she cannot do it.

I can walk
upside down.

I can jump.

I can hop.

I can go.

41

Sticker Sheet 4

Which letter does the word begin with?
Write the letter. Say the word.
Practice writing the letters u, q, e, v, and i.

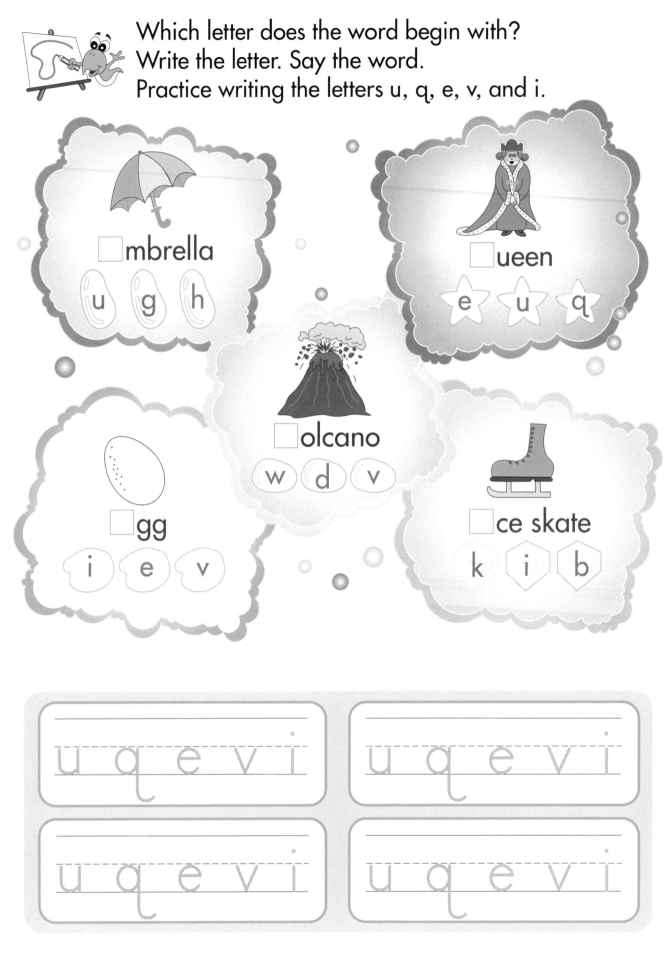

☐mbrella

u   g   h

☐ueen

e   u   q

☐olcano

w   d   v

☐gg

i   e   v

☐ce skate

k   i   b

u q e v i

u q e v i

u q e v i

u q e v i

My Camera

The girl takes some pictures of the pelican.
Stick the stickers to show what she sees.

The pelican likes my camera. Snap.

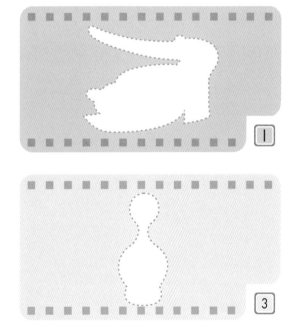

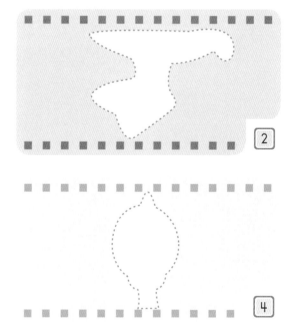

44

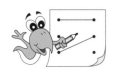

Match the pictures to the words.
Write the words. Say the words.

   •   •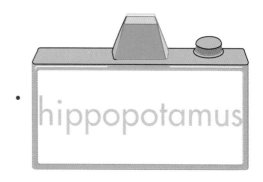

hippopotamus

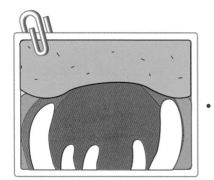   •   •

gorilla

   •   •

giraffe

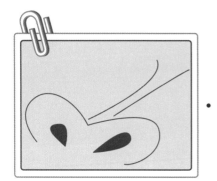   •   •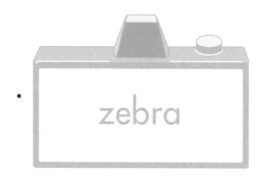

zebra

45

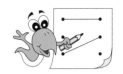

Which letter does the word begin with?
Write the letter. Say the word.
Practice writing the letters x, k, and n.

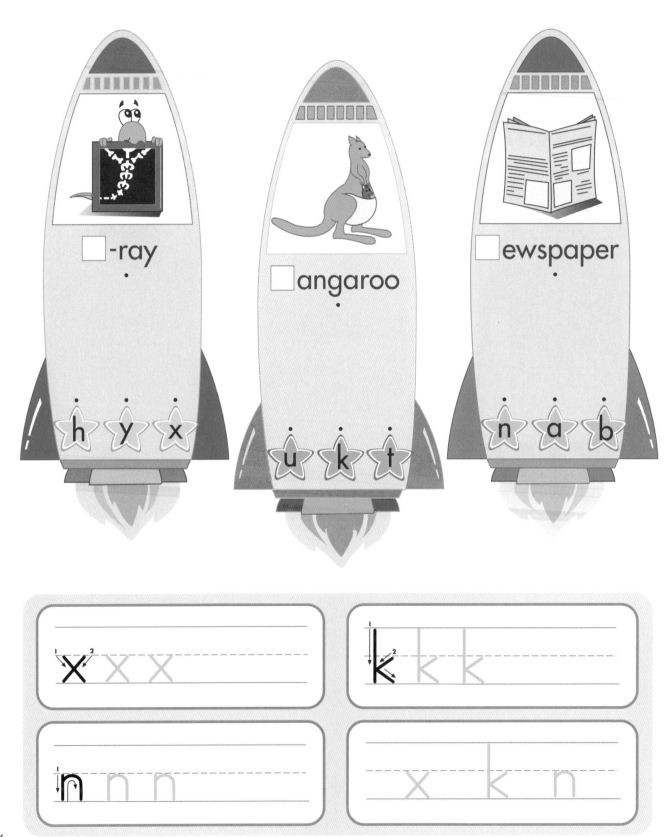

☐-ray

☐angaroo

☐ewspaper

h y x

u k t

n a b

x x x

k k k

n n n

x k n

How many hippos in the cars? Trace the paths.
Stick the stickers. Write the numbers in the boxes.

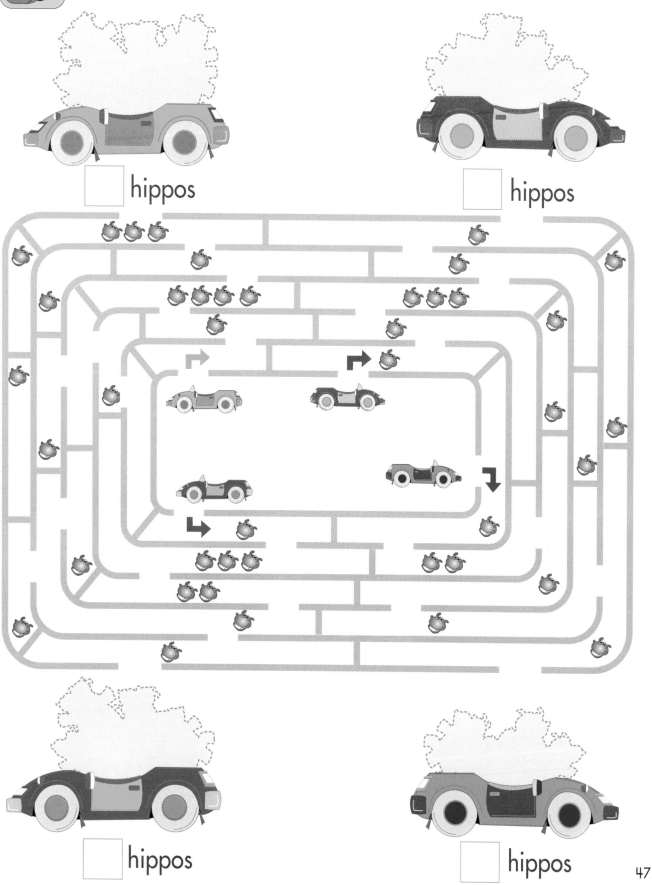

hippos

hippos

hippos

hippos

47

© 2006 Wendy Pye Publishing Ltd

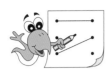 Match the letters to the words. Say the words. Practice writing the letters y, p, and t.

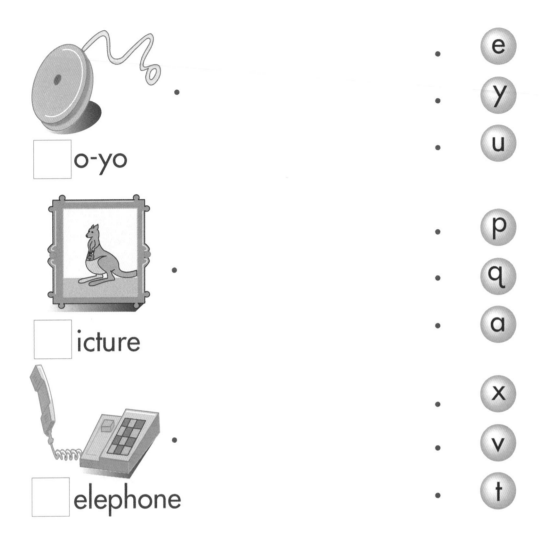

o-yo

e
y
u

icture

p
q
a

x
v

elephone

t

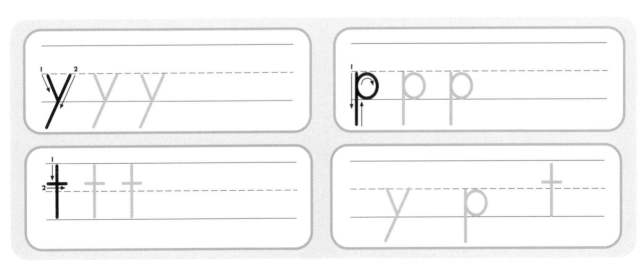

Stick the stickers. Read the words.
Practice writing the letters n, y, t, p, k, and x.

ewspaper

o-yo

elephone

icture

angaroo

-ray

n y t p k x   n y t p k x

n y t p k x   n y t p k x

49

Play the game.

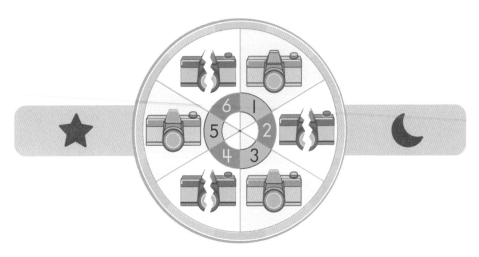

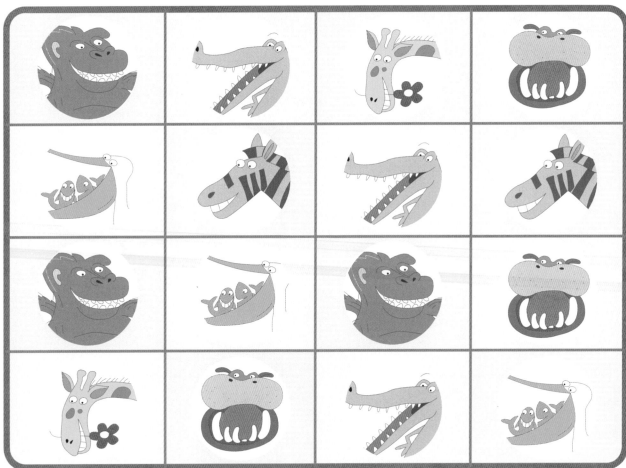

You need: number cube, star and moon stickers

1. Decide who goes first. Choose a star or a moon sticker.

2. Throw the number cube. If you get 1, 3, or 5, say, "The _____ likes my camera. Snap."
   Put a sticker on an animal. If you throw 2, 4, or 6, miss a turn.

3. The first player with four stickers in a row, up or down, is the winner.

50

Look at the pictures. Stick the stickers that match.
Read the sentences.

The _____ likes my camera. Snap!

The _____ likes my camera. Snap!

The _____ likes my camera. Snap!

51

Sticker Sheet 5

Stick the stickers.
Write the words. Say the words.

gorilla

giraffe

zebra

52

Stick the stickers.
What do the animals say?
Say the words.

Tweet!

Moo!

Meow!

Squeak!

Croak!

Woof!

54

Read *"Squeak," Said the Mouse*. Who sits next to whom?
Look at the pictures. Find the pattern.
Stick the stickers. Say the words.

Sticker Sheet 7

Find the upper case letters. Stick the stickers.
Say the words. Practice writing the upper case letters
and the lower case letters.

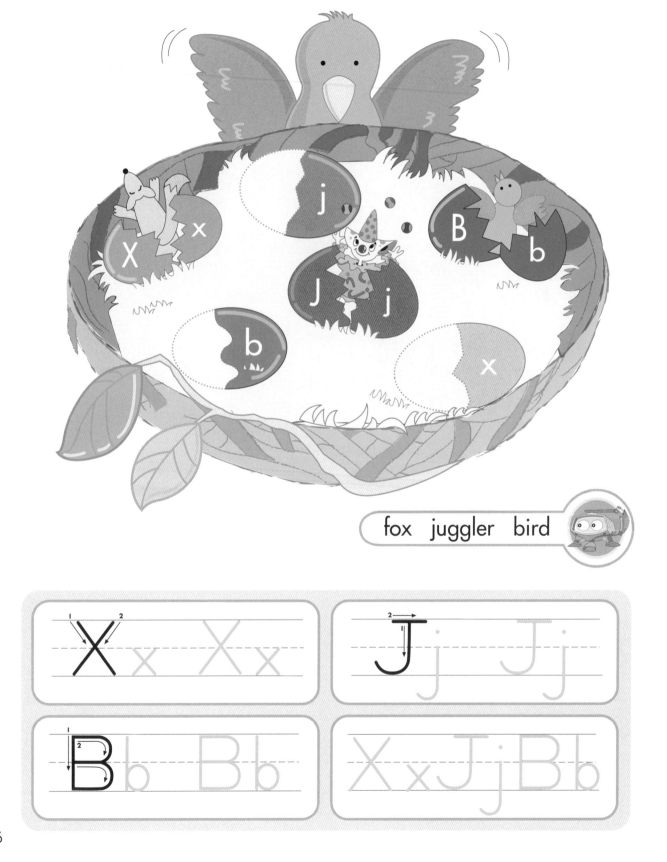

fox   juggler   bird

© 2006 Wendy Pye Publishing Ltd

How many are there?
Stick the stickers.

2

Sticker Sheet 6

Use the Word Bank to find the names of the animals on the fence. Circle the names. Write the missing letters. Say the words.

d (c o w) p i d o g s e e b i r d u n c a t

cow dog bird cat frog mouse

b _ _ d

_ _ ow

d _ _

_ _ o g

c _ _ t

m _ _ s e

o m f r o g n e m o u s e o p

Stick the upper case letters that match.
Say the words. Practice writing the upper case letters
and the lower case letters.

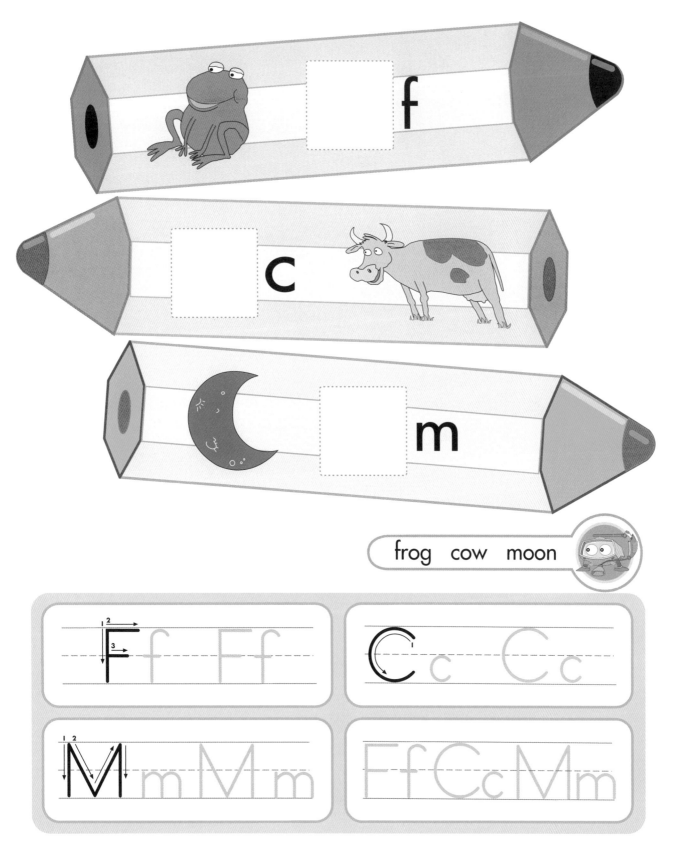

frog   cow   moon

Sticker Sheet 6

Play the game.

You

"Woof," said the dog.

Me

"Meow," said the cat.

You need: crayons, number cube
1. Choose a picture and decide who goes first.
2. Throw the number cube. Color in the number on your picture. Say, "Meow," said the cat. "Woof!" said the dog.
3. If you get a number that is not in your picture, miss a turn.
4. The first player to color all their pictures is the winner.

60

Color the pictures.
Write the words. Say the sentences.

"Moo," said the cow.

"Croak," said the frog.

"Tweet," said the bird.

61

Stick the stickers. Say the words.
Practice writing the upper case letters
and the lower case letters.

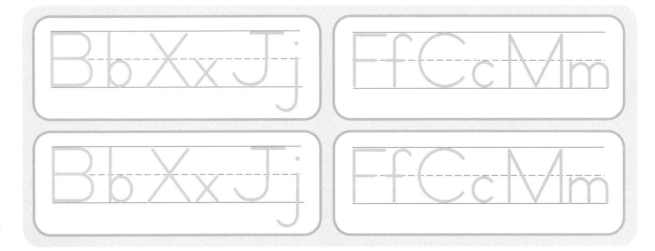

ball   x-ray   jellyfish   family   cake   mouse

62

The Balloon

Read *The Balloon*. Match the letters to the words.
Stick the stickers. Read the words.

In what order do they get out of the balloon?
Follow the path through the clouds.

Write the number next to the picture.

65

Stick the upper case letters that match. Say the words.
Practice writing the upper case letters
and the lower case letters.

sun   ant   ring

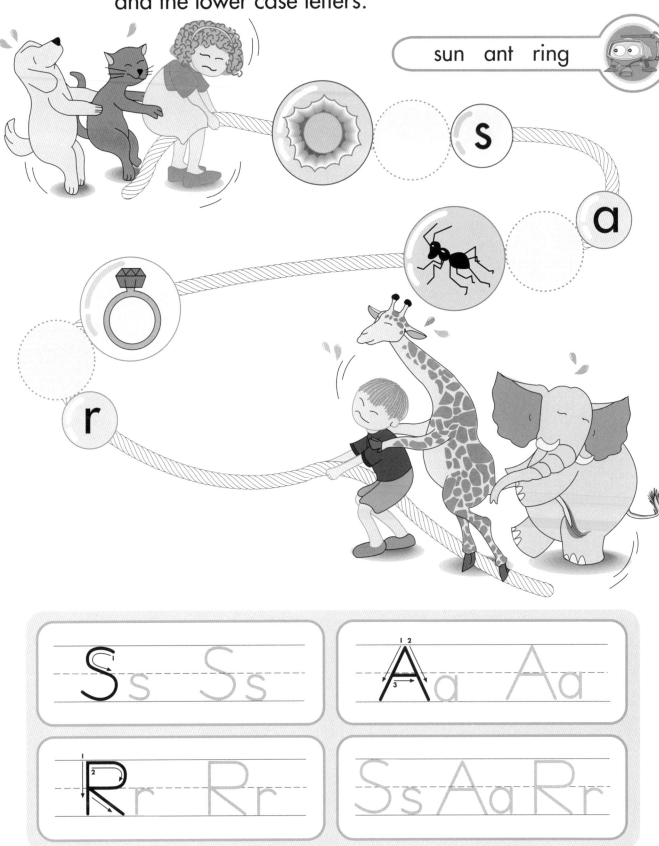

Stick the stickers.
Write the words. Say the words.

elephant

giraffe

girl

boy

dog

cat

67

Sticker Sheet 6

Join the dots. Write the words. Say the words.

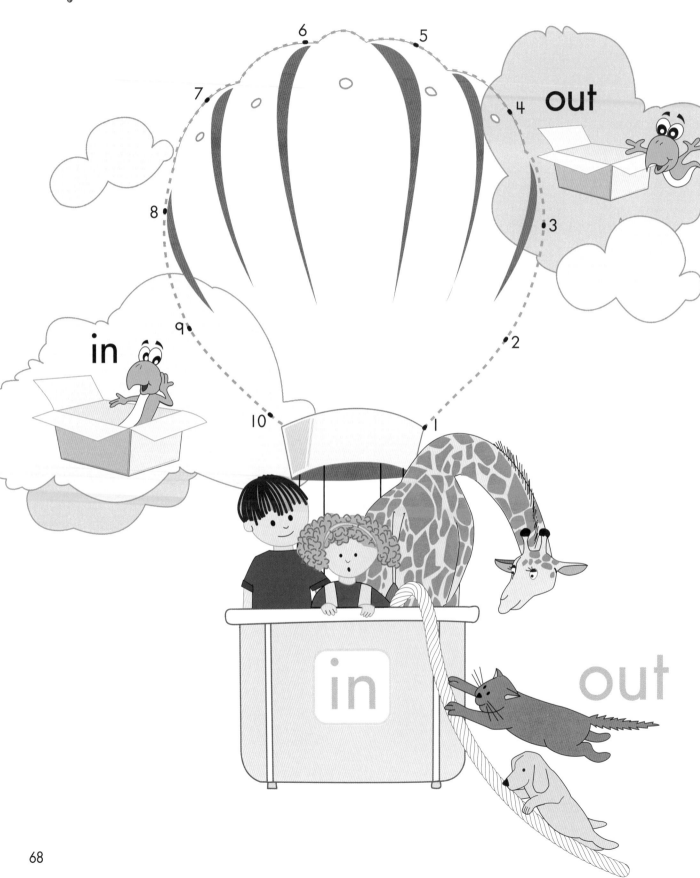

Stick the letters that match the words. Practice writing the upper case letters and the lower case letters.

hat

donut

umbrella

69

Sticker Sheet 7

Play the game.

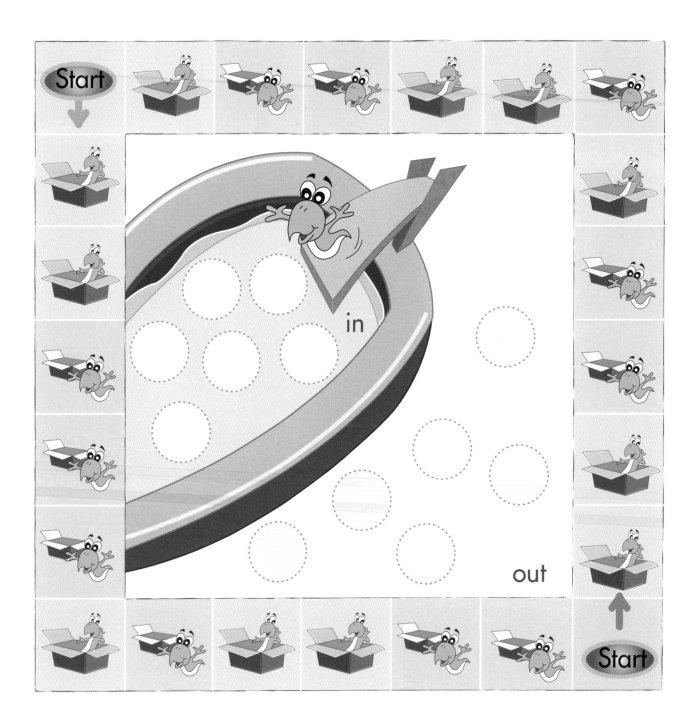

You need: counters, number cube

1. Decide who goes first. Put your counter on **Start.** Throw the number cube.
2. Move your counter the number of places. If you get an "in" picture, say, "The cat got in."
   Stick your cat sticker on an "in" spot. If you get an "out" picture, say, "The cat got out."
   Stick your cat sticker on an "out" spot.
3. The first player to use all their stickers is the winner.

70

Sticker Sheet 7

© 2006 Wendy Pye Publishing Ltd

Who got out of the balloon?
Write the words. Say the words.

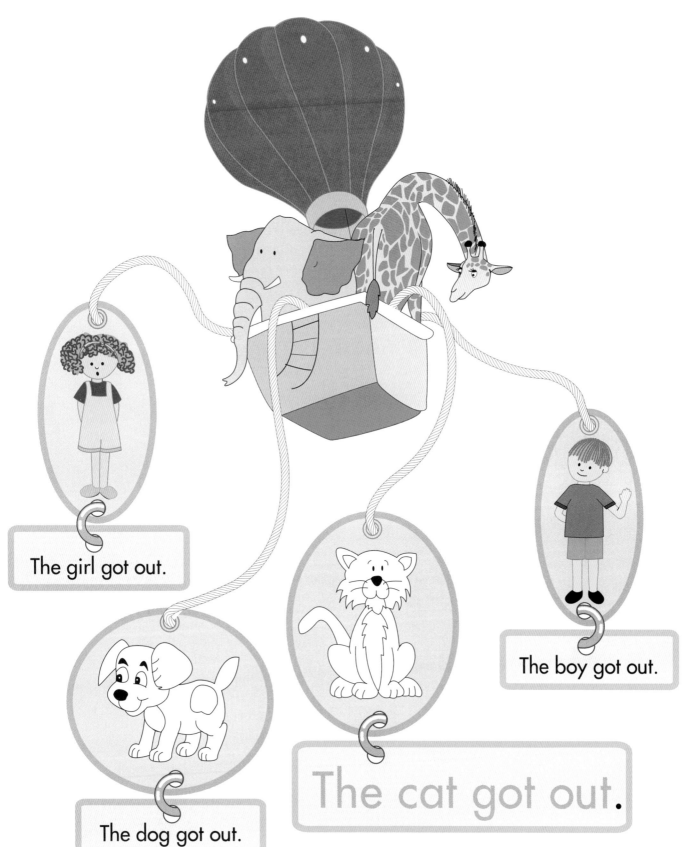

The girl got out.

The dog got out.

The cat got out.

The boy got out.

71

 Match the words to the pictures. Say the words.
Practice writing the upper case letters and
the lower case letters.

Ss Aa

Hh Dd

Rr Uu

sock   alligator   hat   digger   robot   umbrella

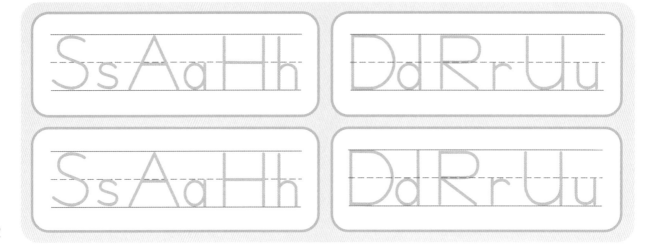

SsAaHh DdRrUu

SsAaHh DdRrUu

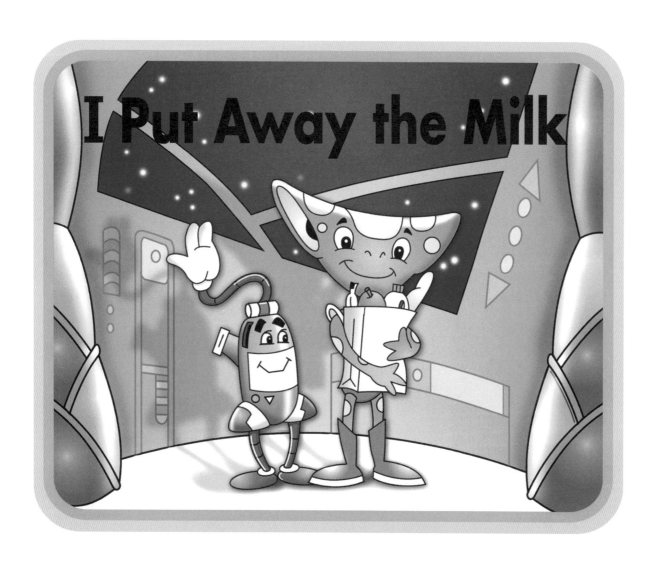

73

Read *I Put Away the Milk.*
Stick the stickers to match the words.

milk   peas

eggs   cheese

apple

bread

FOOD

Stick the word **away** on Lettergetter's board.
Say the word. Write it in the sentences. Say the sentences.

I walk _____.

I fly _____.

I put _____.

I run _____.

75

© 2006 Wendy Pye Publishing Ltd

Match the letters to the words. Say the words.
Practice writing the upper case letters
and the lower case letters.

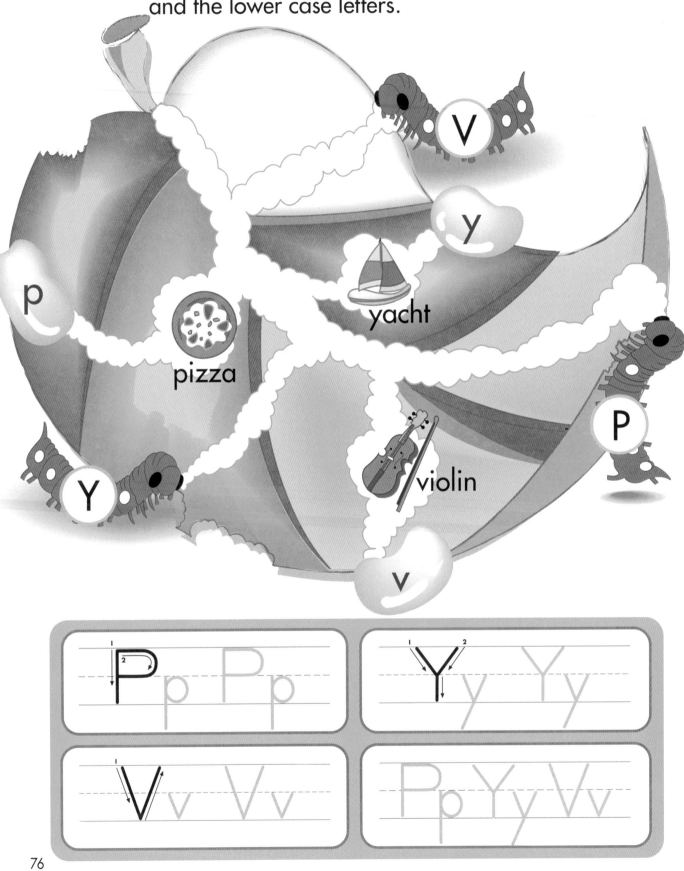

V

y

p

yacht

pizza

violin

P

Y

v

P p P p

Y y Y y

V v V v

P p Y y V v

76

Stick the letter stickers to match the pictures.
Say the words. Practice writing the upper case letters
and the lower case letters.

 pirate yo-yo volcano kangaroo ice cream goat egg

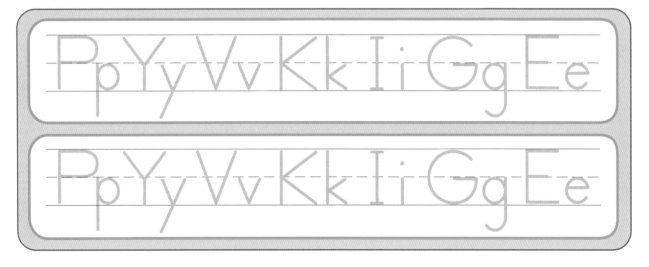

77

Sticker Sheet 8

Stick the missing upper case letter stickers. Say the words.
Practice writing the upper case letters
and the lower case letters.

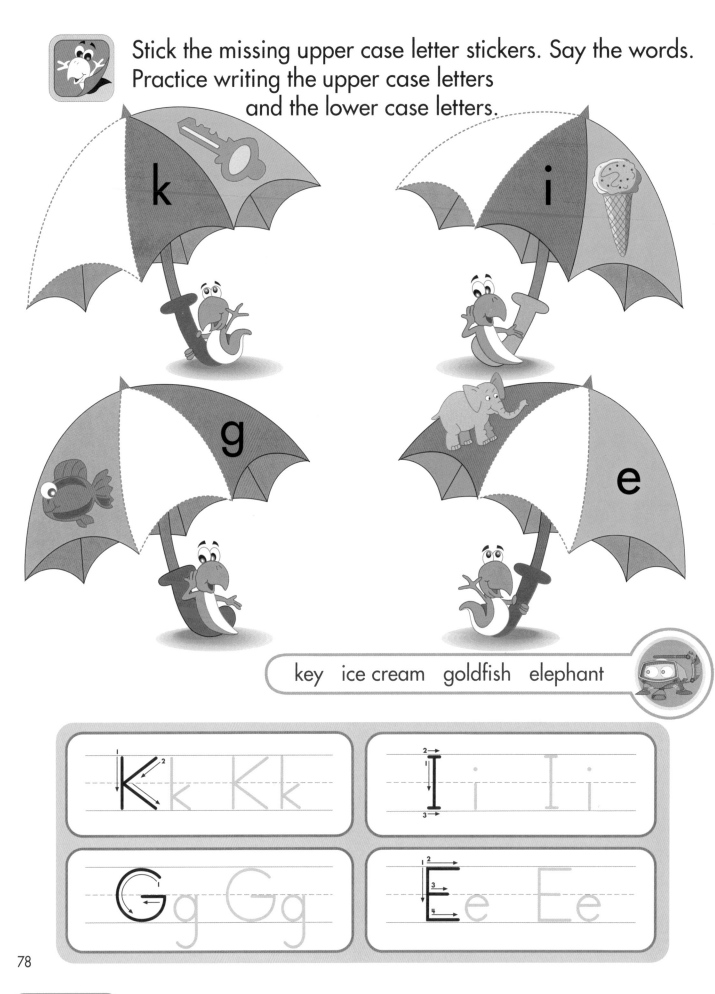

key   ice cream   goldfish   elephant

Sticker Sheet 9

How much juice is in the pitcher?
Stick the stickers to match the words.

Not enough

Too much

Just enough

79

Sticker Sheet 9

Play the game.

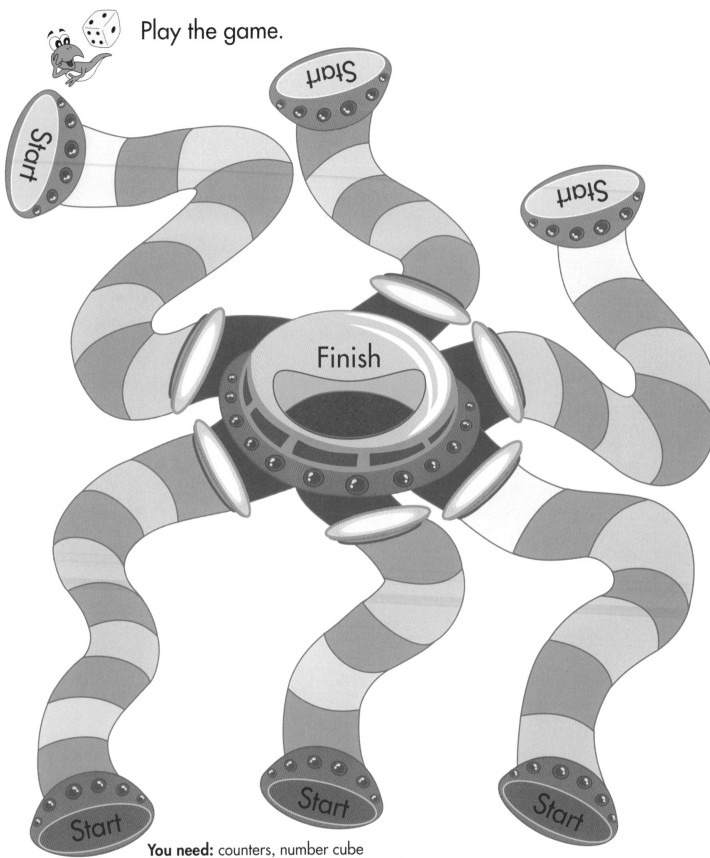

Finish

Start

Start

Start

Start

Start

Start

You need: counters, number cube
1. Stick the food stickers together to make counters.
   Choose 3 counters each and put them on **Start.**
2. Throw the number cube and move one of your counters the same number of places.
3. When a counter lands on a plate, say, "I put away the _____."
   Put the food in the mouth.
4. The first player to use up all their counters is the winner.

80

Sticker Sheet 8

Fold the page along the dotted line. Cut along the solid lines with scissors. Write the words. Say the words.

apple

I put away the apple.

eggs

I put away the eggs.

cheese

I put away the cheese.

bread

I put away the bread.

81

Cut and fold. Write and read the words.

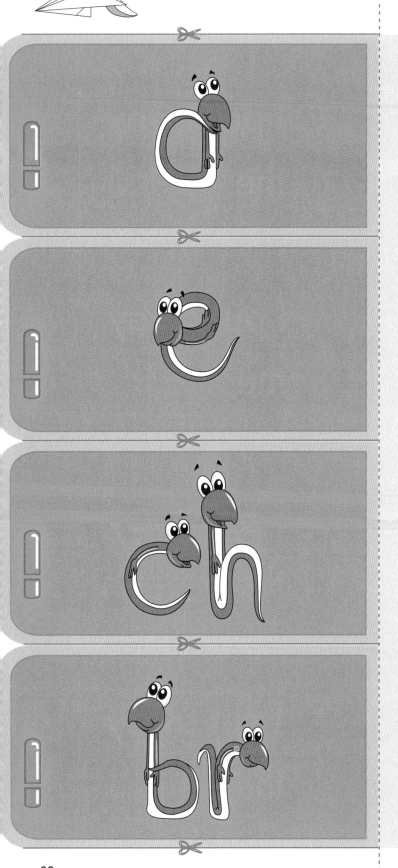

apple

eggs

cheese

bread

Under the Table

Read *Under the Table*. Look at the shapes.
Find the pictures and color them.

| table | bike | chairs | stairs | mouse | house | mat |

Stick the stickers to finish the picture. Trace the words. Say the words. Match the words to the pictures.

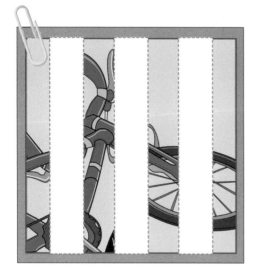

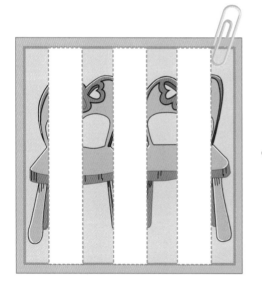

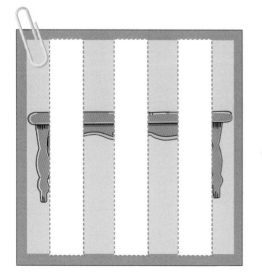

85

Sticker Sheet 9

Stick the upper case letter stickers that match. Say the words. Practice writing the upper case letters and the lower case letters.

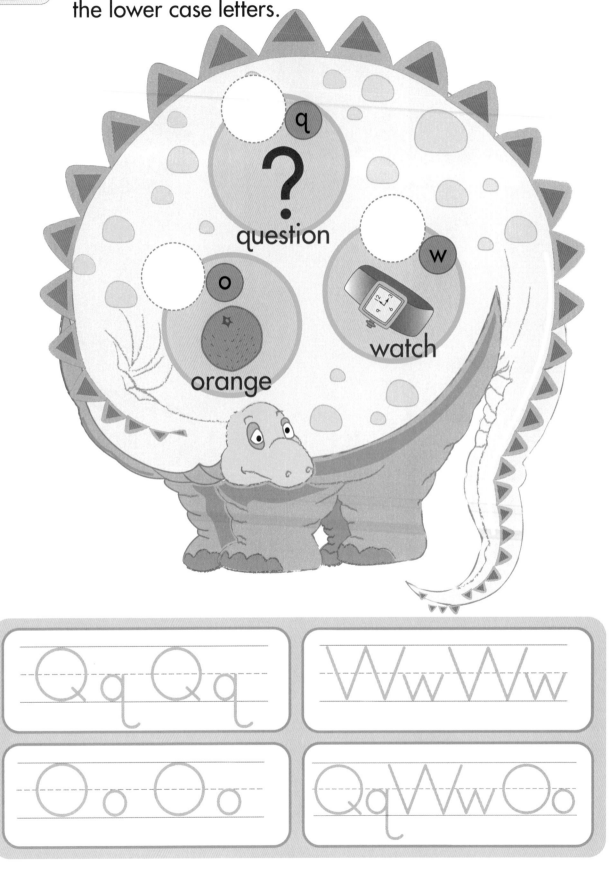

question

orange

watch

86

Where is the mouse: on or under?
Stick the stickers that match the pictures.
Write the words. Say the words.

The mouse is under the house.

87

Sticker Sheet 8

 Read *Under the Table*. Write the words to finish the sentence. Say the sentences.

1 The mouse is under the mat.

2 The mouse is under the house.

3 The mouse is under the stairs.

4 The mouse is under the bike.

"I am safe | u | | | | | | | | | | | | | | | | ,"
said the mouse.

Stick the upper case letters that match. Say the words.
Practice writing the upper case letters
and the lower case letters.

tiger zebra nurse lizard

89

Sticker Sheet 8

Play the game.

You need: number cube, stickers

1. Decide who goes first. Choose cat or mouse stickers.
2. Throw the number cube. Put a sticker on the picture with the same number.
   Say, "I am under the ___."
3. The first player to stick all their stickers is the winner.

90

Sticker Sheet 9

 Color the mouse. Write the words. Say the words.

The mouse is
under the table.

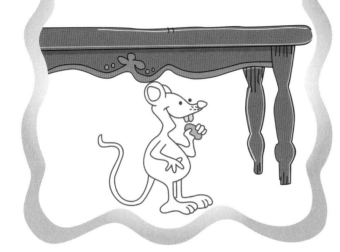

The mouse is
under the chairs.

The mouse is
under the mat.

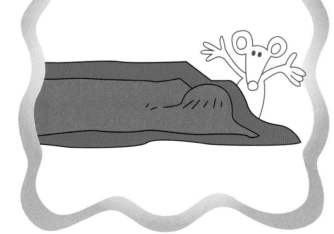

The mouse is
under the bike.

Stick the stickers that match. Name the pictures.
Practice writing the upper case letters
and the lower case letters.

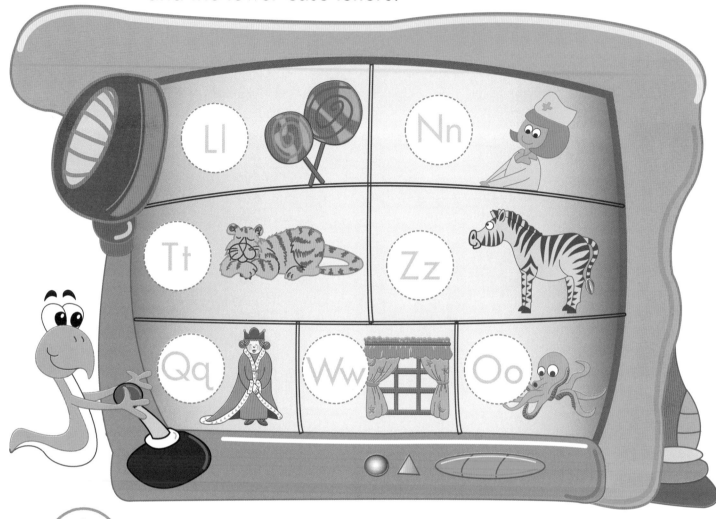

Ll   Nn

Tt   Zz

Qq   Ww   Oo

 lollipops nurse tiger zebra queen window octopus

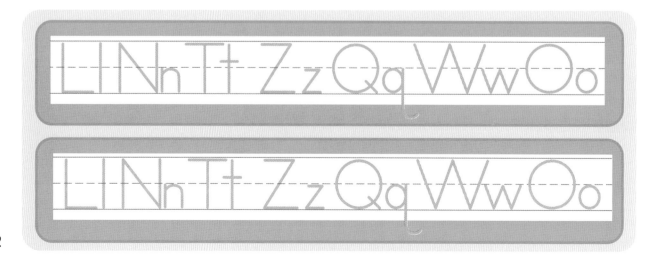

Ll Nn Tt Zz Qq Ww Oo

Ll Nn Tt Zz Qq Ww Oo

92

Donald the Dragon

 Read *Donald the Dragon*. Color Donald.
Say, "Donald the Dragon..." Write the words.

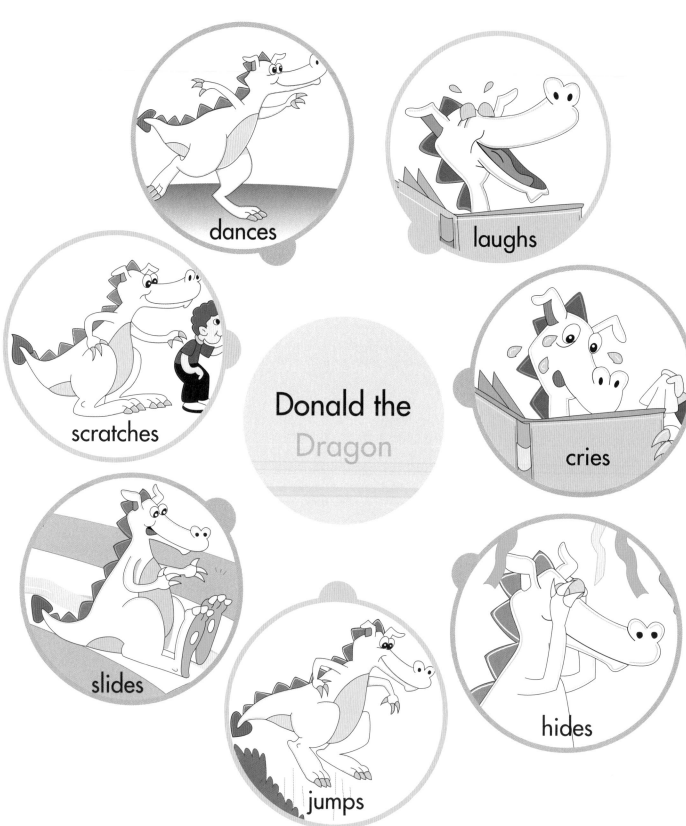

dances

laughs

scratches

Donald the

Dragon

cries

slides

jumps

hides

Stick the stickers that match the pictures.
Say, "Everyone…"

Sticker Sheet 10

Stick the stickers in the correct spaces.
Say the letter names. Write the letters.

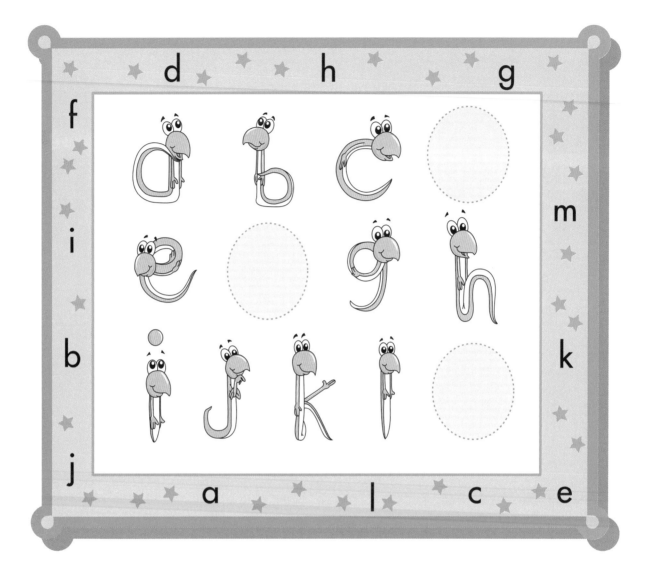

a b c d e f g h i j k l m

a   m

Sticker Sheet 11

Stick the stickers.
Write the words.
Say the words.

Sticker Sheet 11

Color the letters. Say the letter names.
Write the letters.

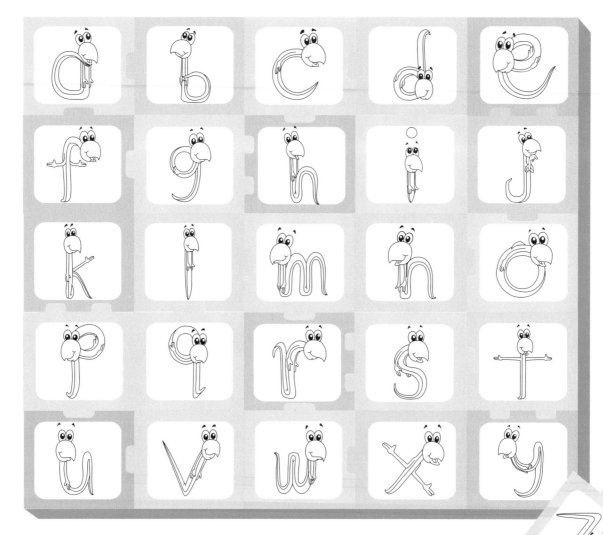

a b c d e f g h i j k l m

n o p q r s t u v w x y z

Stick the stickers in the correct spaces.
Say the letter names. Write the letters.

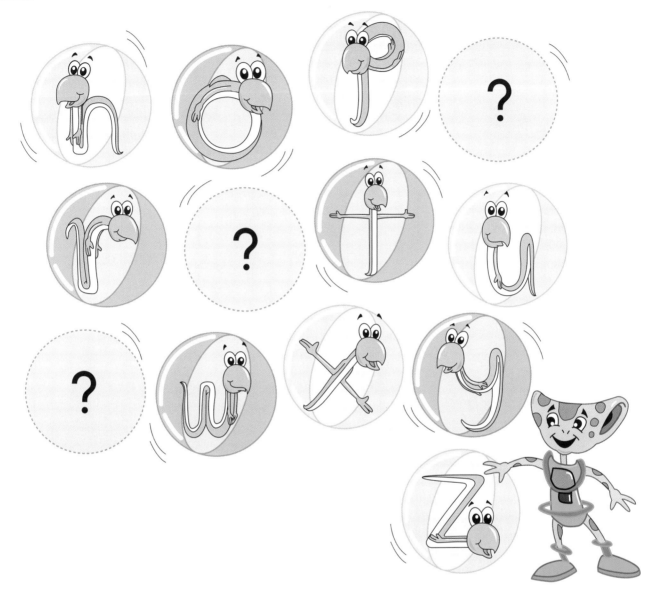

n o p q r s t u v w x y z

n   z

Sticker Sheet 10

Play the game.

① cries	④ dances	② scratches
⑥ slides	③ laughs	① cries
⑤ jumps	④ dances	⑥ slides

You need: red and blue stickers, number cube
1. Decide who goes first. Choose the red or blue stickers and stick them together to make 6 counters.
2. Throw the number cube and put a counter on the same number.
3. Say, "When Donald the Dragon _____, everyone _____."
4. The first player to get 3 counters in a row, up or down, is the winner.

100

Sticker Sheet 10

© 2006 Wendy Pye Publishing Ltd

Read the words. Write the words.
Stick the stickers. Say the words.

When Donald the Dragon

When Donald the Dragon
laughs, everyone laughs.

laughs   dances

101

Write the words. Read the words.
Stick the stickers. Say the words.

Donald the Dragon cries.

When

Donald the Dragon cries,

Sticker Sheet 11

Look at Me, Mom!

Write the words. Help the monkeys go through the maze to find the pictures that match the words.

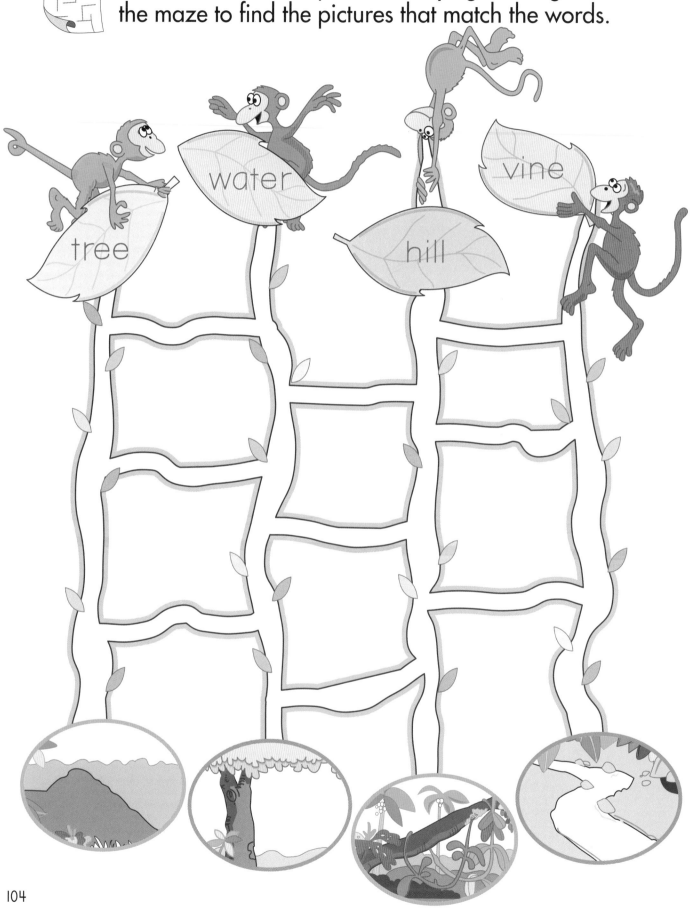

tree

water

hill

vine

104

© 2006 Wendy Pye Publishing Ltd

What can each monkey do?
Stick the stickers that match the pictures.

105

Sticker Sheet 11

Stick the stickers in the correct spaces.
Say the letter names.

Aa Bb Cc Dd

Ee Ff Gg

Ii Jj Ll

Mm Nn Oo Pp

Qq Ss Tt

Uu Vv Xx

Yy Zz

106

Look at the pictures. Stick the stickers that match.

Family

107

Inside or outside?
Stick the sticker that matches the pictures.

Sticker Sheet 11

Write the words. Say the words.

I can run up the hill.

I can roll down the hill.

up

down

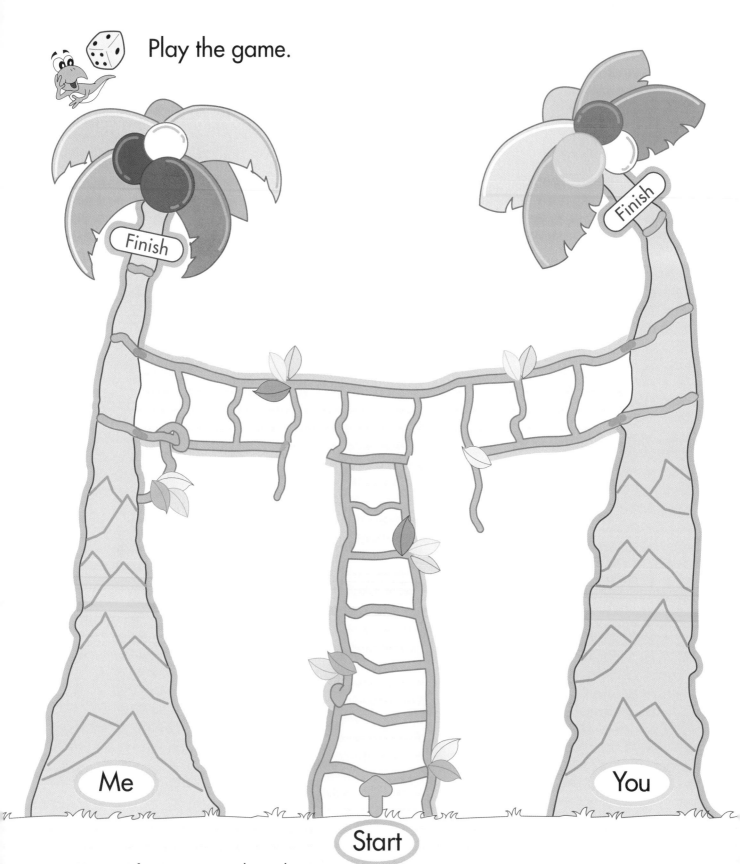

Play the game.

You need: counters, number cube

1. Decide who goes first. Stick the stickers to make 3 counters each. Put your counter on **Start.**
2. Throw the number cube. If you get an even number, move 2 spaces.
   If you get an odd number, move 1 space. If you land on a broken space, go back to **Start.**
3. When you reach **Finish,** put your counter on the tree.
4. The first player to put 3 counters on the tree is the winner.

110

Look at the pictures. Stick the stickers that match.

Sticker Sheet 11

Write the words. Say the words.
Stick the stickers that match.

I can jump over the water.

I can run up the hill.

I can climb up the tree.

I can swing on the vine.

112

Hide and Seek

Read *Hide and Seek*.
Stick the stickers to label the animals. Say the words.

dog

Stick the stickers to match the pictures.
Write the letters to finish the words.
Say the words.

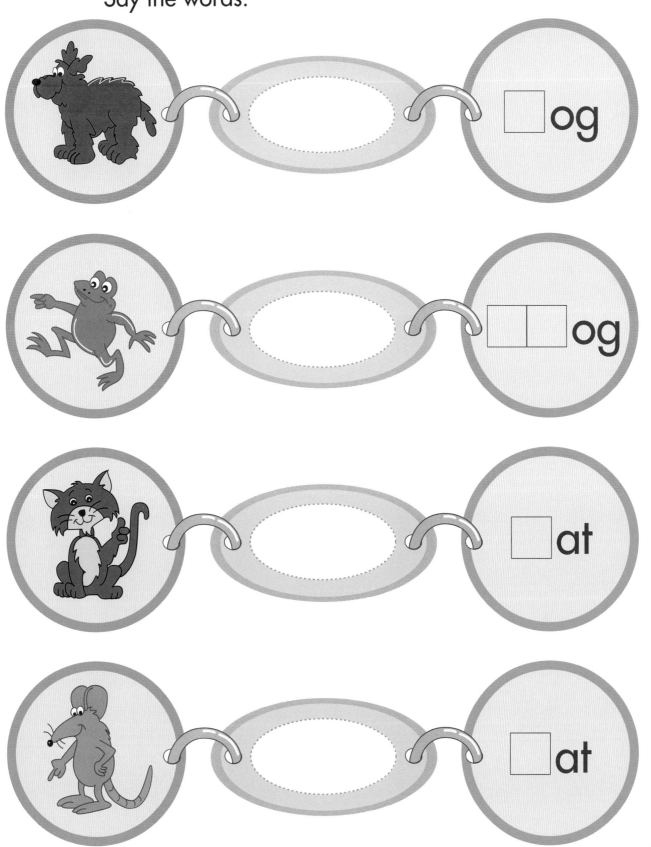

☐og

☐☐og

☐at

☐at

115

Sticker Sheet 12

Stick the stickers in the correct spaces.
Write the letters. Say the words.

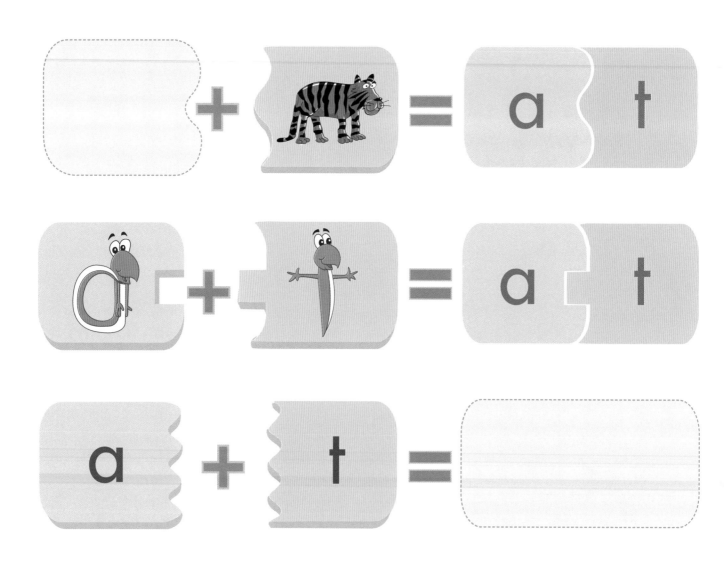

$$\boxed{} + \boxed{\text{(cat)}} = \boxed{a \quad t}$$

$$\boxed{\text{(d)}} + \boxed{\text{(t)}} = \boxed{a \quad t}$$

$$\boxed{a} + \boxed{t} = \boxed{}$$

cat

mat

hat

rat

Stick the stickers of the animals in order of size.
Write the words. Say the words.

shortest

tallest

117

Read the words. Look at the pictures.
Stick the stickers that match.

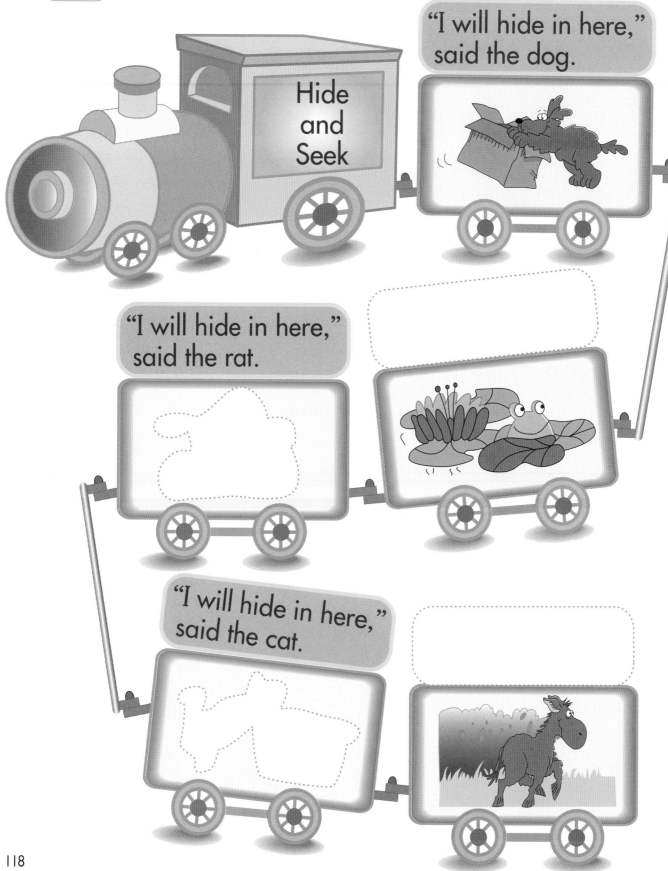

"I will hide in here," said the dog.

Hide and Seek

"I will hide in here," said the rat.

"I will hide in here," said the cat.

118

Find and color the leaves with words in the **-at** word family.
Make words that match the pictures below.

m	h	c	r

___ at   ___ at   ___ at   ___ at

119

Play the game.

You need: stickers, number cube

1. Choose your play board. Take 5 stickers each.
2. Throw the number cube. If you get an odd number, say, "I will hide in here," said the _____. Put the sticker on your game board.
3. If you get an even number, you miss a turn.
4. The first player to stick all their stickers on their board is the winner.

120

Read the words. Look at the pictures.
Stick the stickers that match.

I will hide in here.

No, you will not hide in here!

No, you will not hide in here!

Sticker Sheet 12

Look at the pictures. Find the
words on the scarf. Circle them. Write the words.
Say the words.

u c a t m s p (h a t) u z e q m a t c i

f g a r a t n j k l n o y e z u t

mat   rat   hat   cat

My Guide Dog

Read *My Guide Dog.*
Stick the stickers to label the pictures.

124

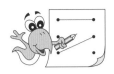

Write the words. Say the words.
Match the words to the pictures.

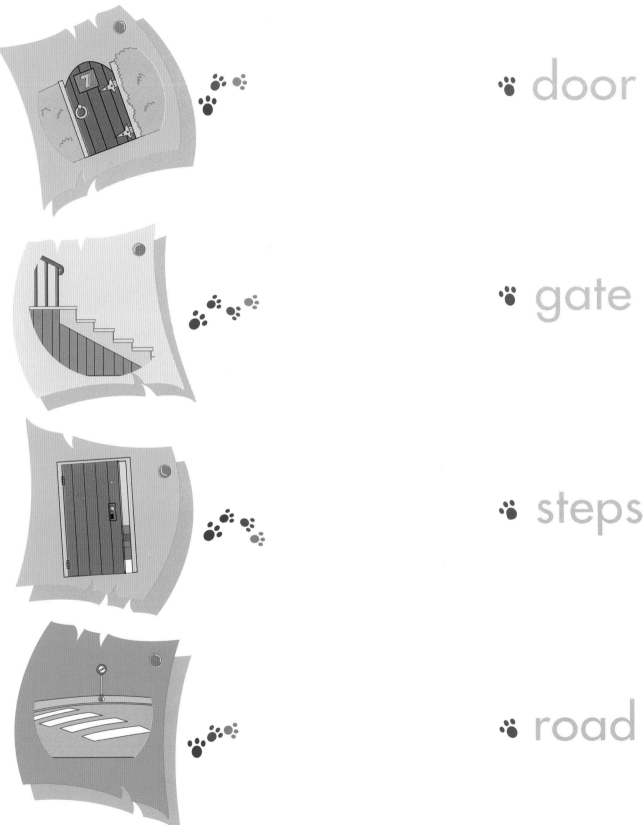

door

gate

steps

road

Stick the stickers to make **-an**.
Finish the words. Say the words.

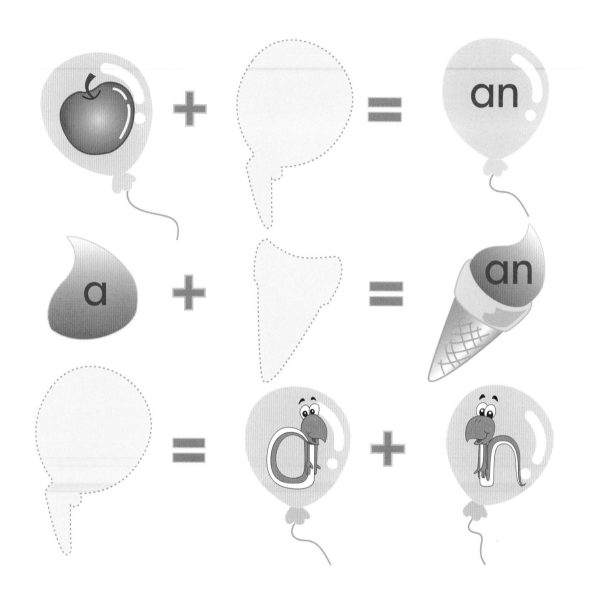

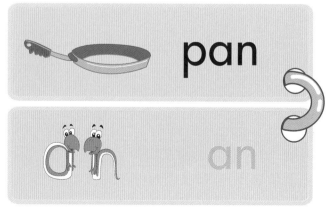

Stick the stickers to join the pictures together.
Write the word. Read the sentences.

I can't see the car but Penny can.

I can't see the gate but Penny can.

127

Sticker Sheet 12

Look at the pictures. Say the words.
Circle True or False.

Color the words in the **-an** word family.
Write the letters to finish the words below.
Say the words.

p	m	f

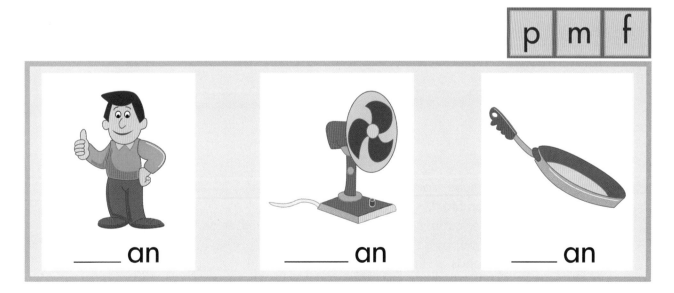

____ an   ____ an   ____ an

Play the game.

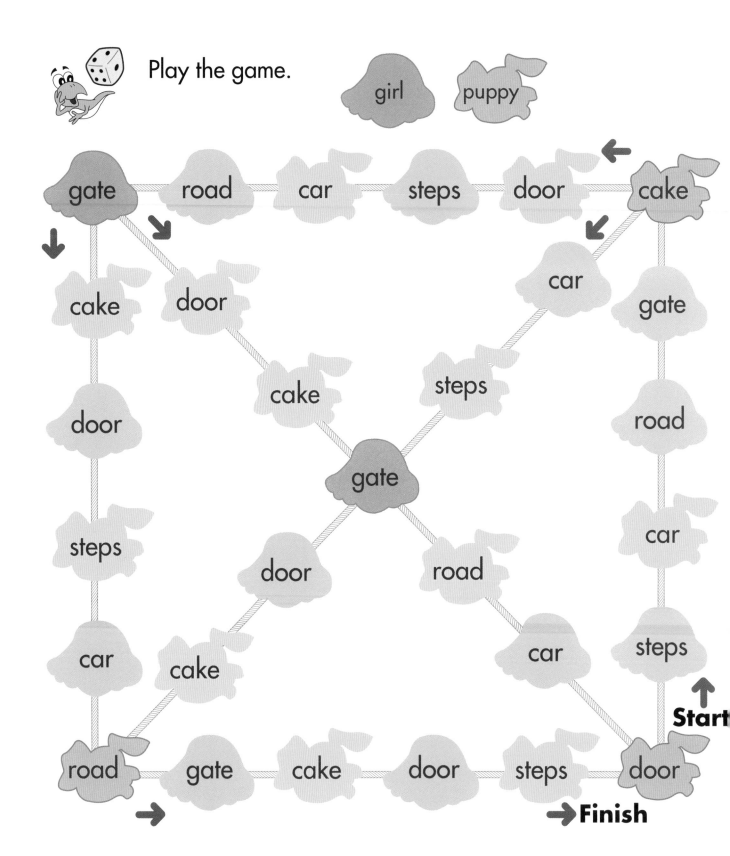

girl   puppy

gate   road   car   steps   door   cake

cake   door   car   gate

door   cake   steps   road

gate

steps   door   road   car

car   cake   car   steps

Start

road   gate   cake   door   steps   door

→ Finish

You need: number cube, counters
1. Put the counter on **Start.**
2. Throw the number cube. Move your counter the number on the number cube.
   If you land on a puppy say, "I can see the _____."
3. If your counter lands on the girl, say, "I can't see the _____."
4. The player who arrives at **Finish** first wins the game.

130

Stick the stickers that match the words.
Write the words. Read the sentences.

I can't see the door
but Penny _____ .

I can't see the steps
but Penny _____ .

I can't see the car
but Penny _____ .

I can't see the road
but Penny _____ .

131

Sticker Sheet 13

Look at the picture clues.
Find the words and circle them.
Write the words in the boxes.

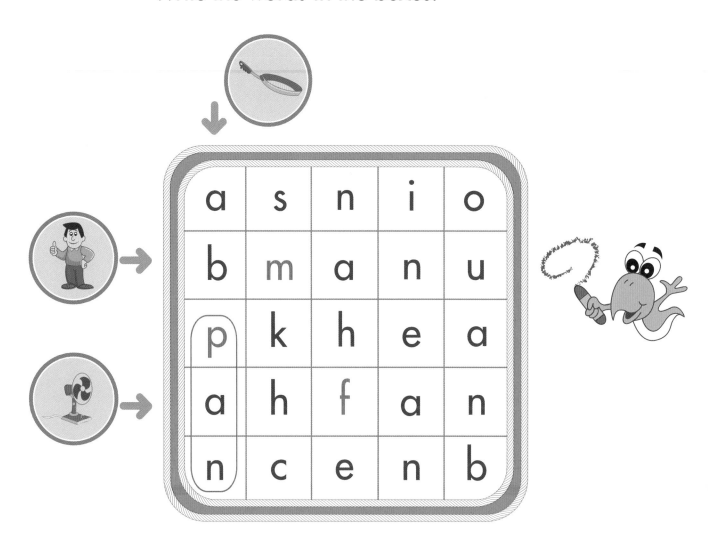

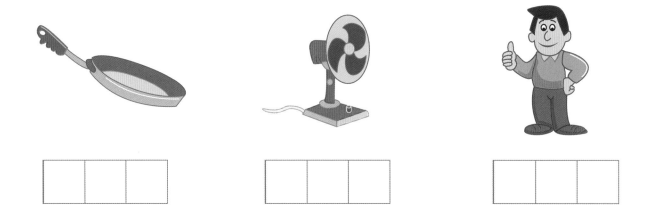

Spots and Stripes

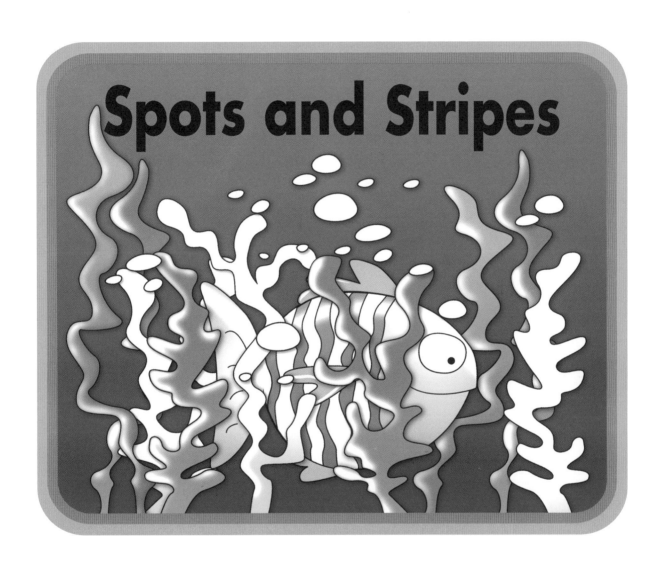

Read *Spots and Stripes*. Do the animals have spots or stripes? Match the animal names to the bath towels.

snake

zebra

leopard

tiger

deer

fish

fish   tiger   deer   snake   zebra   leopard

 Find and color the animals in the pictures.
Stick the stickers. Write the words.

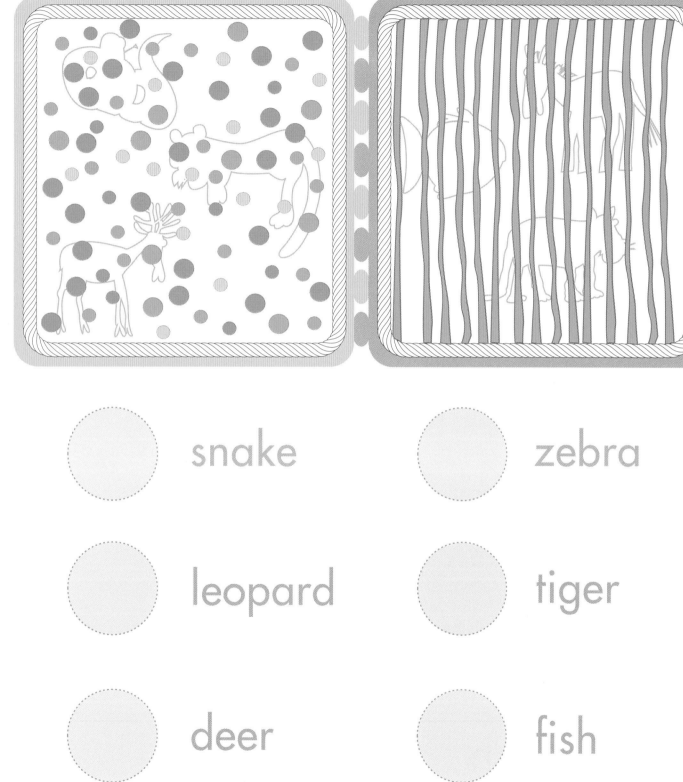

snake

zebra

leopard

tiger

deer

fish

135

Sticker Sheet 14

Stick the sticker to make -**ake**.
Finish the words. Say the words.

$$a + \text{(apple)} + e = ake$$

cake

snake

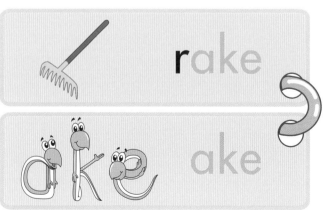

rake

ake

136

Color the words in the **-ake** word family.
Write the letters to finish the words below.
Say the words.

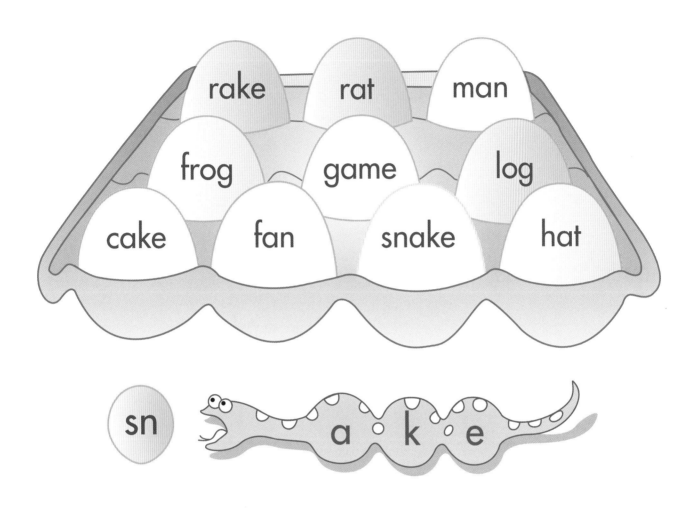

rake	rat	man
frog	game	log
cake	fan	snake	hat

sn   a   k   e

| c | r | sn |

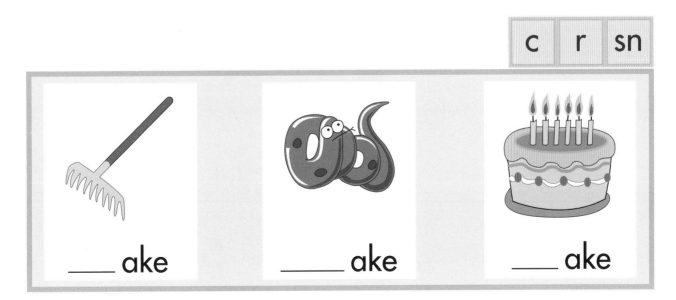

___ake   ____ake   ___ake

Count the spots and stripes. Stick the stickers.
Say the sentences.

The leopard has ☐ spots.

The snake has ☐ spots.

The zebra has ☐ stripes.

The fish has ☐ stripes.

one	two	three	four	five	six
1	2	3	4	5	6

138

Look at the pictures.
What happened to Lettergetter when he went swimming?
Stick the sticker to show what Lettergetter said. Say the word.

139

© 2006 Wendy Pye Publishing Ltd

Sticker Sheet 14

Play the game.

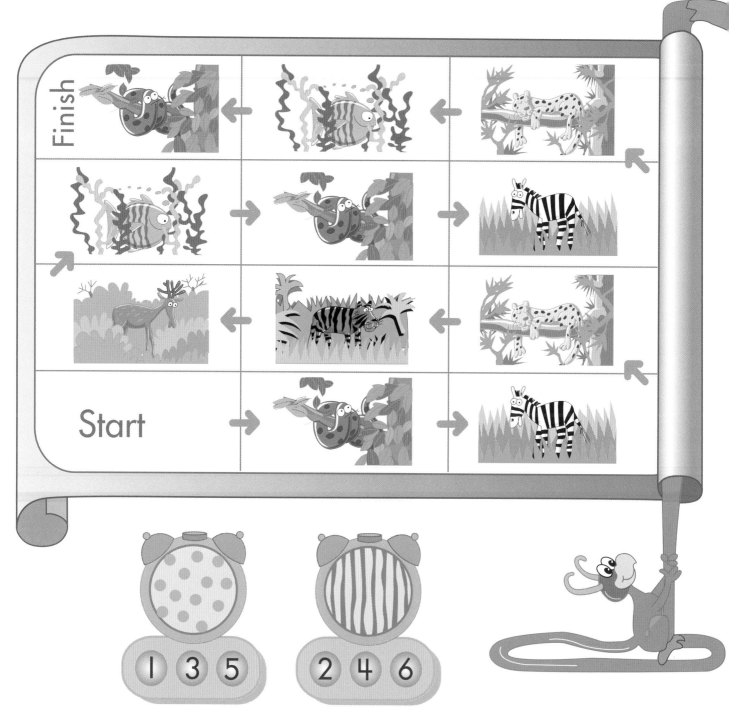

You need: number cube, counters

1. Decide who goes first. Put the counter on **Start.**
2. Throw the dice. If you get an odd number, move your counter onto an animal with spots. If you get an even number, move your counter onto an animal with stripes. Say, "_____ help the _____ to hide in the _____."
3. The first player to reach **Finish** is the winner.

Write the words to finish the sentences. Use the Word Bank.
Stick the sticker that matches the words.
Say the sentences.

Sp _____ help this l _____
to hide in the sh _____ .

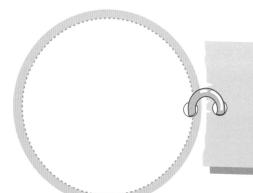

Str _____ help this t _____
to hide in the j _____ .

Sp _____ help this d _____
to hide in the b _____ .

| Spots | tiger | leopard | Stripes |
| jungle | deer | bushes | shadows |

141

Sticker Sheet 14

Look at the picture clues. Find and circle the words.
Write the words in the boxes. Say the words.

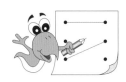 Read *Where?* Write the words.
Read the words. Match them to the pictures.

diver   •   •

pirate   •   •

firefighter   •   •

astronaut   •   •

144

Stick the stickers to label the pictures.

145

Stick the stickers to make **-og.**
Write the letters. Read the words.

o + g = og

dog

fog

frog

log

146

Where is the firefighter going with the cat?
Go through the maze. Stick the stickers on the path.
Answer the question.

Sticker Sheet 14

How many animals are there?
Stick the stickers. Count and say the numbers.

three

four

four

five

two

one

148

Find and color the pictures in the tree stump.
Write the letters to finish the words below.
Say the words.

| d | f | fr | l |

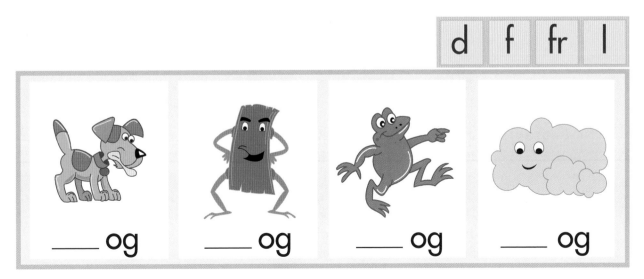

___og   ___og   ___og   ___og

149

Play the game.

You need: number cube, stickers

1. Stick the stickers together to make 12 counters.
   Choose Zina or Lettergetter and decide who goes first.
2. Throw the number cube. The number on the number cube has a hand picture for the game "Paper, rock, scissors". When the other player throws the cube, do the hand actions and whoever wins puts their counter somewhere on the board.
3. Then they say, "Where is the _____ going with the _____?"
4. The first player to finish a line (up or down) is the winner.

150

Stick the stickers that match the words.
Write the words to finish the questions.
Ask the questions.

Where is the
a_____
going with the
goose?

Where is the
b_____
going with the
dog?

pirate	firefighter	diver	astronaut	butcher

151

Sticker Sheet 15

Find and circle the words. Use the Word Bank.
Write the words in the boxes. Say the words.

p b a e f g d o g m l o g
u c f r o g a z f o g j k m e n g

fog log dog frog

And on My Hand

Where is **And**? Stick the stickers.
Write the words. Say the words.

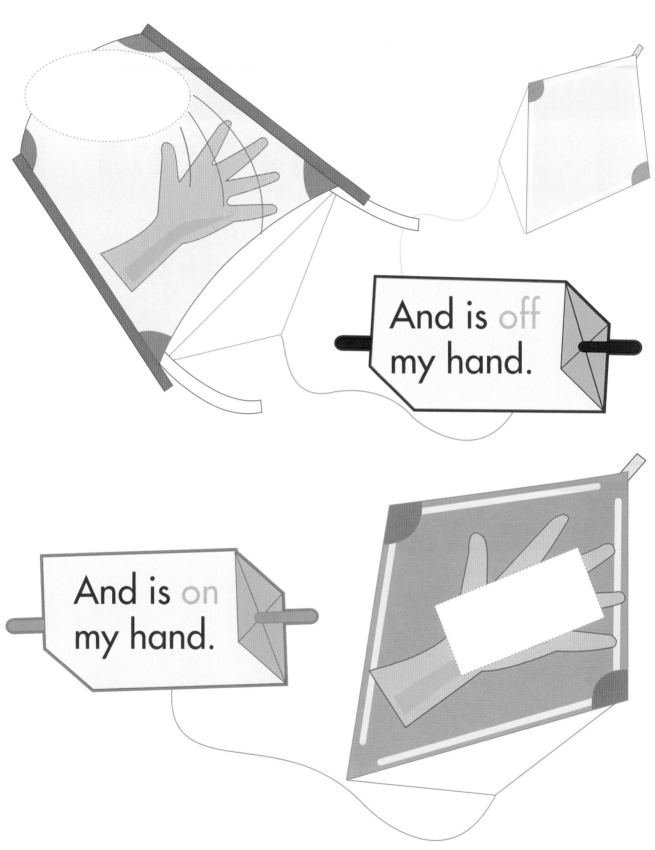

And is off
my hand.

And is on
my hand.

154

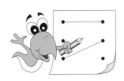

Read *And on My Hand.* Write the words.
Say the words. Match the words to the pictures.

and is in the sand •

•

and is on her hand •

•

and is on her band •

•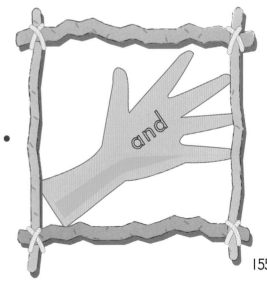

155

Stick the stickers to make **and.**
Write the letters to finish the words.
Say the words.

h**and**

b**and**

s**and**

and

156

Where is the monkey? Stick the stickers.
Write the words. Say the sentences.

Look!!

"Look, the monkey is off the bed."

"Look, the monkey is on the bed."

157

Stick **and** on the pictures.
Write the words. Say the sentences.

"Look, Grandma,
and is on my hand."

"Look, Grandma,
and is off my hand."

"Look, Grandma,
and is in the sand."

"Look, Grandma,
and is on my band."

Find and color the words in the **-and** word family.
Write the letters to finish the words below.
Say the words.

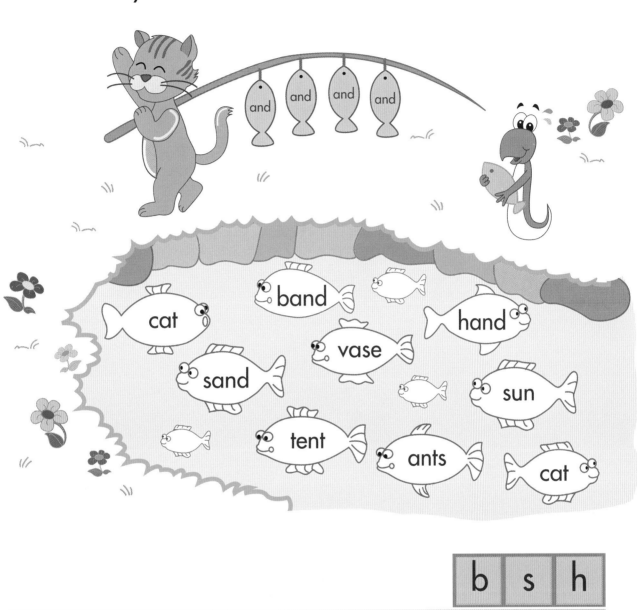

b	s	h

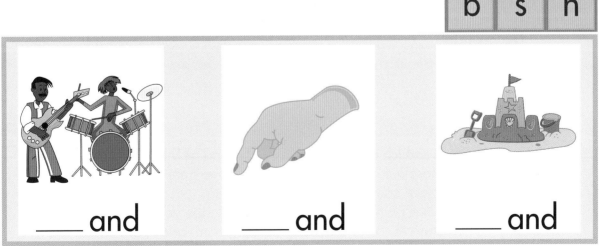

___ and   ___ and   ___ and

159

Play the game.

You need: counters

1. Choose which character you will be (Zina or Lettergetter) and place a counter on them. Decide who goes first.
2. Move your counter onto the first picture.
3. To win the point, say the words that describe your picture. For example, point 1: "Look, teacher/mom, **and** is on/off the chair."
4. The player with the most points in the game is the winner.

Stick the stickers to finish the sentences.
Say the sentences.

" _____ , Grandma,
and is _____ my hand."

"Look, _____ ,
and is _____ my hand."

" _____ , Grandma,
and is _____ my band."

"Look, _____ ,
and is _____ my hand."

Find and circle the words. Use the Word Bank. Write the words in the boxes.

a u b **a n d** j k l m s **a n d** z c d

band sand hand

e f g **h a n d** q r t w y a c x

163

Stick the stickers to match the words.
Write and say the words.

carrots

bananas

berries

porridge

nuts

164

 Read *Someone Ate Our Food*. Write the words. Say the words.

raccoons

monkeys

rabbits

bears

squirrels

animals

165

Stick the stickers to make **ate.**
Write the letters to finish the words.
Say the words.

 gate

 skate

plate

ate

Sticker Sheet 17

Whose book is this?
Stick the stickers. Say the words.

This is a book.

This is [ ] book.

my

This is [ ] book.

our

167

© 2006 Wendy Pye Publishing Ltd

Sticker Sheet 17

Write the words. Say the sentence.
Now draw your own picture
and write a sentence about it.

"Someone ate our carrots," said the rabbits.

Find and color the words in the **-ate** word family.
Write the letters to finish the words below.
Say the words.

rake

skate

dog

frog

cat

snake

cake

fan

can

log

gate

plate

sand

frog

| g | pl | sk |

____ate

____ate

____ate

169

Play the game.

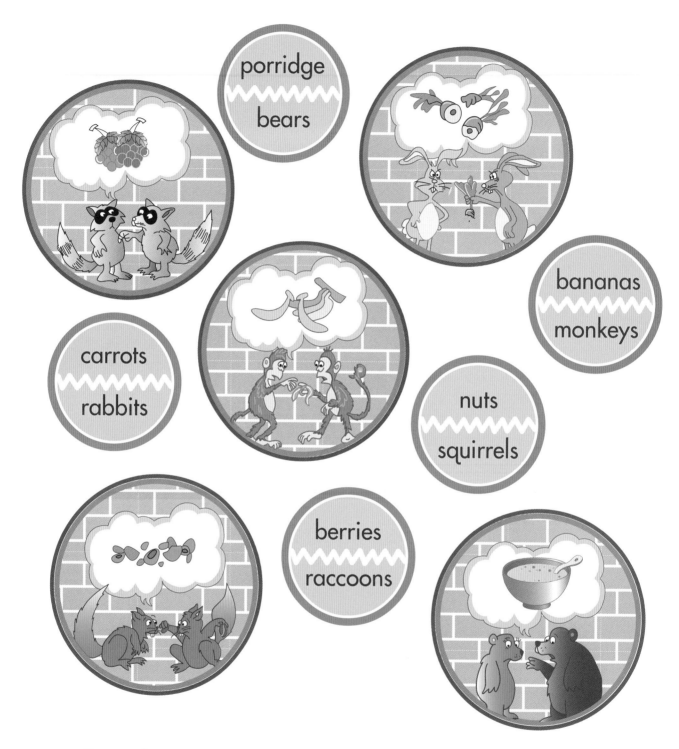

You need: counters

1. Decide who goes first. Drop a counter onto the page from a height of 8 inches.
2. If it falls on a big circle, you get 1 point. If it falls on a small circle, you get 2 points. Say, "Someone ate our _____," said the _____.
3. Write down your points. The player with the most points is the winner.

170

Stick the stickers. Write the words to match the picture. Say the sentence.

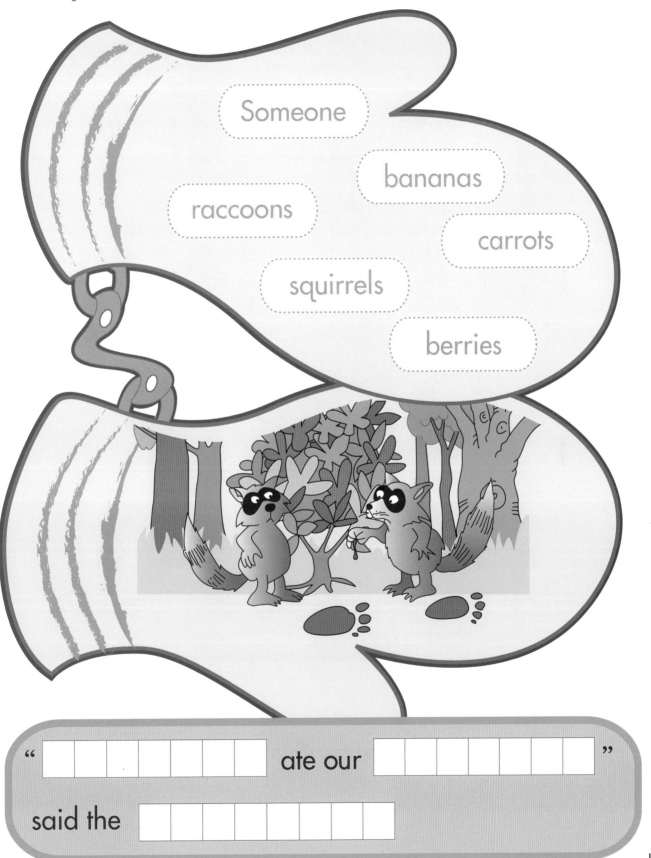

Someone

bananas

raccoons

carrots

squirrels

berries

" ☐☐☐☐☐☐☐ ate our ☐☐☐☐☐☐☐ "

said the ☐☐☐☐☐☐☐

171

Find the words in the soup and circle them.
Use the Word Bank. Write the words in the boxes.

skate plate gate ate

u b o n g a t e i j k
s k a t e b z n p
u a t e b z n p l a t e

The Puppies

Read *The Puppies*. Write the words.
Stick the stickers that match.
Say the words.

black puppy

white puppy

brown puppy

174

Use the coordinate grid to find the letters.
Write them in the boxes. Say the words.

	🔵(spotted)	🔵(striped)	★	◆	■	⬤
?	b	u	o	p	w	e
!	m	s	y	t	c	a
*	g	r	h	l	i	n

🔵! ★? ◆! ★* ⬤? 🔵*

| m | | | | | |

🔵* ■* 🔵* ◆*

| | | | |

🔵! ⬤! ⬤*

| | | |

◆? 🔵? ◆? ◆? ■* ⬤? 🔵!

| | | | | | | |

🔵? ★? ★!

| | | |

■? ★? 🔵! ⬤! ⬤*

| | | | | |

175

Stick the stickers to make **-ack**.
Write the letters to finish the words.
Say the words.

-ack

a +

k +

pack

sack

snack

ack

176

Write the words to finish the sentences.
Stick the stickers that match.
Say the sentences.

The man had
a white puppy.

Mother dog _____
five puppies.

The boy _____
a big puppy.

The woman _____
a brown puppy.

177

Sticker Sheet 18

Find and color the words
in the **-ack** word family.
Write the letters to finish the words below.
Say the words.

gate

snack

rat

plate

pack

snack

pack

ack

night

fan

sack

yummy
yum

sand

frog

sack

light

snake

rake

hand

sn

s

p

___ack

___ack

___ack

Stick the stickers that match the picture.
Say the words.

Sticker Sheet 19

Play the game.

big

black

white

brown

little

You need: scissors, pencil, paper
1. Cut out the cards down the side of the page to make the point cards.
2. Mix the cards up, turn them upside down, and put two cards on each card shape.
3. Decide who will go first. Take turns choosing a card and say, "I want the _____ one."
4. Score points according to how many apples are on the cards. Take away points if you get a lemon card. The game is over when all of the cards are used.

180

What are Zolar and Zina saying?
Choose the words from the Word Bank.
Write and say the words. Stick the stickers.

Sticker Sheet 18

Look at the picture clues.
Find and circle the words.
Write the words in the boxes.
Say the words.

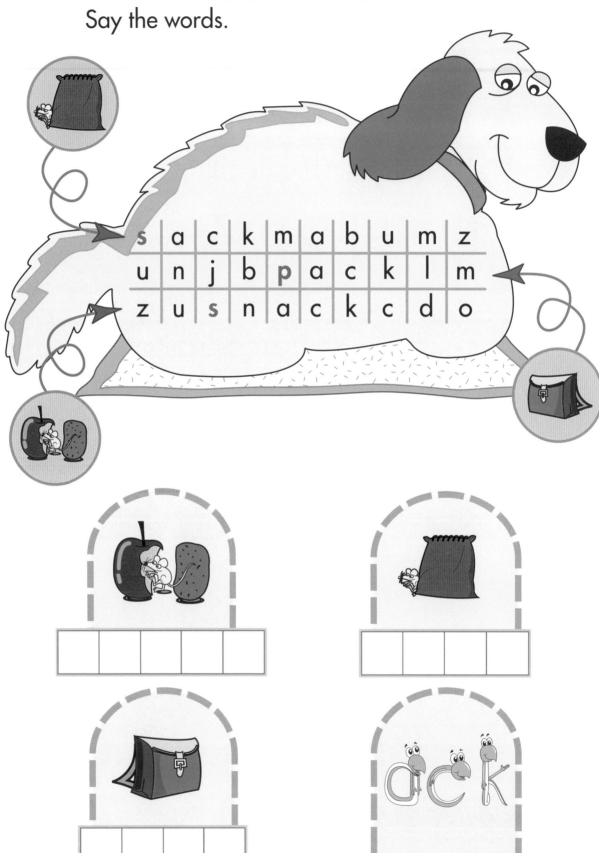

s	a	c	k	m	a	b	u	m	z
u	n	j	b	p	a	c	k	l	m
z	u	s	n	a	c	k	c	d	o

Mrs. McGuire's Muffins

Write the words. Say the words.
Stick the stickers to match the words.

Muffins

just right

hard

soft

small

burned

184

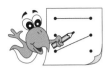

Read *Mrs. McGuire's Muffins*. Write the words. Say the words. Stick the stickers on the plates to match the words.

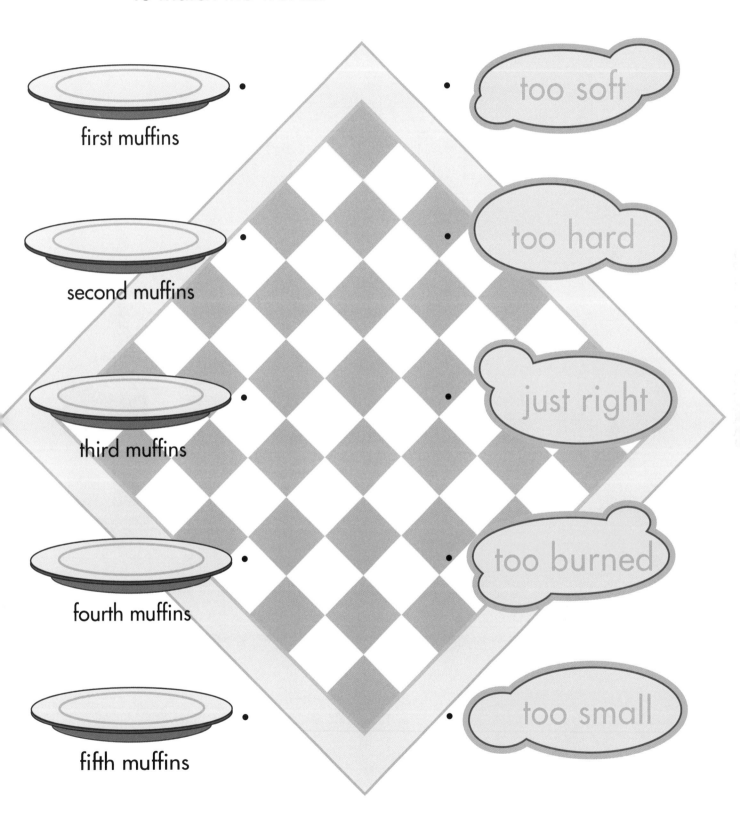

first muffins

second muffins

third muffins

fourth muffins

fifth muffins

too soft

too hard

just right

too burned

too small

185

© 2006 Wendy Pye Publishing Ltd

Stick the sticker.
Write the words in the **-ight** word family.
Say the words.

-ight

i g h t

-ight

-ight   -ight

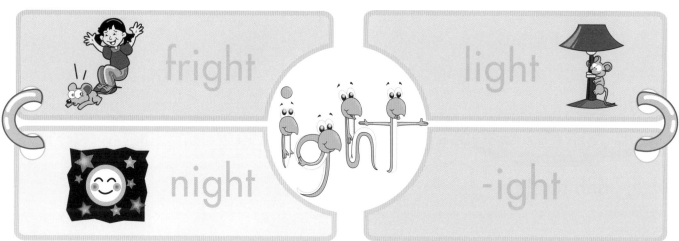

fright   light

night   -ight

Sticker Sheet 19

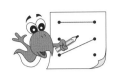 Write the words. Say the sentences.
Match the sentences to the pictures.

Mrs. McGuire
made a boat.

Zina _____
a car.

Lettergetter
_____ a fish.

187

What did Mrs. McGuire do to make the muffins?
Stick the stickers in the correct order.
Say a sentence about each picture.

Muffin Cookbook

1 first

2 second

4 last

3 third

Find and color the words in the **-ight** word family.
Write the letters to finish the words.
Say the words.

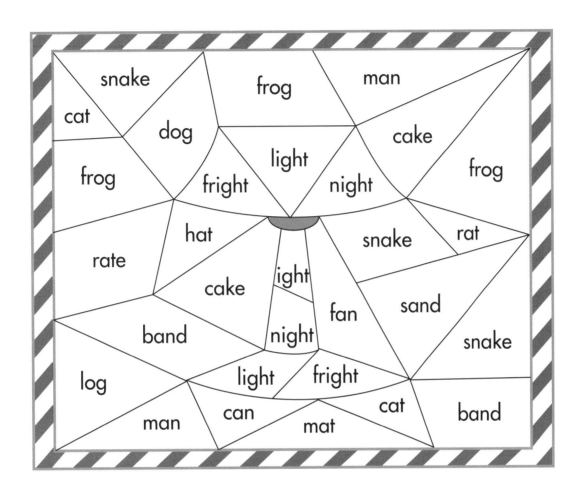

snake	frog	man
cat	dog	cake
frog	fright	light	night	frog
hat	snake	rat
rate	cake	ight	snake
band	night	fan	sand	snake
log	light	fright	cat	band
man	can	mat		

| **fr** **n** **l** | ___ight | ___ight | ___ight |

Play the game.

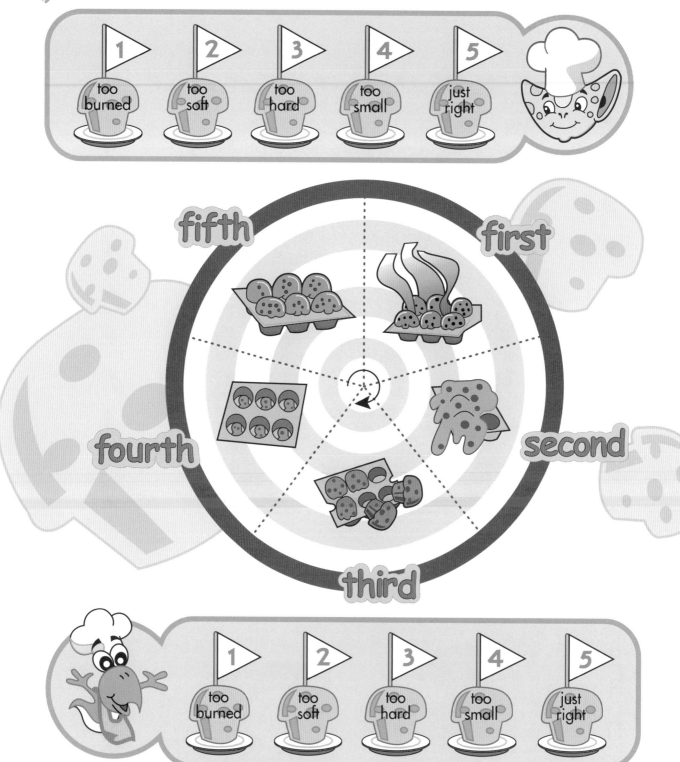

You need: number cube

1. Choose either Lettergetter or Zolar for your character. Decide who goes first.
2. Throw the number cube. If you throw 1, say, "The first muffins were too burned." Then color the first flag. Repeat for numbers up to 5.
3. If you throw 6 or a number that already has a colored flag, miss a turn.
4. The player who colors the most flags after 8 turns is the winner.

Stick the stickers and write the words to finish the sentences. Say the sentences.

Mrs. McGuire made some muffins.

Mrs. McGuire made some muffins.

Mrs. McGuire ☐ some ☐ ☐ .

191

© 2006 Wendy Pye Publishing Ltd

Look at the picture clues.
Find and circle the words.
Write the words in the boxes.

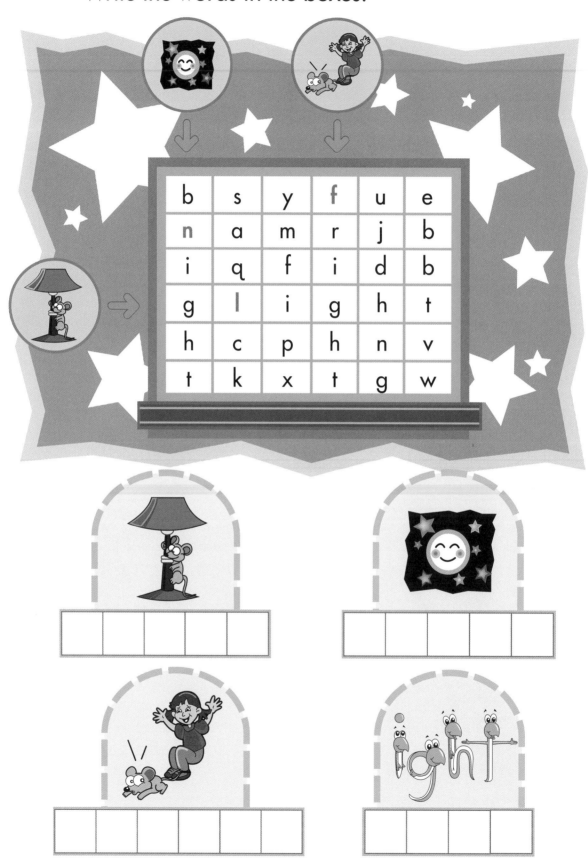

b	s	y	f	u	e
n	a	m	r	j	b
i	q	f	i	d	b
g	l	i	g	h	t
h	c	p	h	n	v
t	k	x	t	g	w

The Week It Rained

Read *The Week It Rained.*
Stick the stickers on the days that match the pictures.

Monday

WET PAINT.

Saturday

 Write the words to label the people.

farmer

gardener

painter

farmer

builder

police officer

camper

Stick the stickers to make **fr-**.

Write the letters to finish the words.
Say the words.

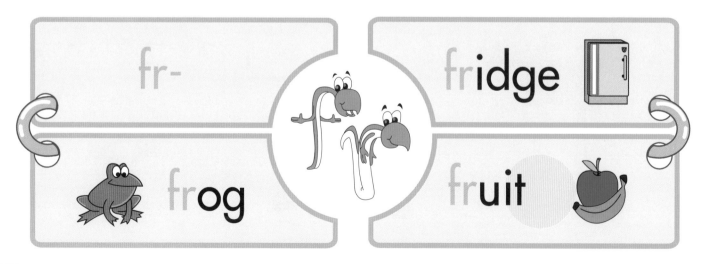

fr-

fr**og**

fr**idge**

fr**uit**

Help the ants go through the maze.
Make words that begin with **fr-**.
Write the letters to finish the words. Say the words.

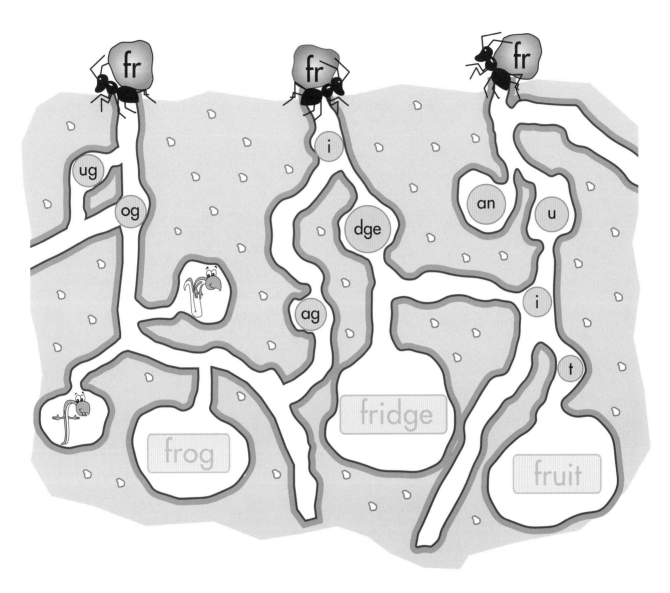

fr **ug**
fr **og**
fr **i**
fr **dge**
fr **ag**
fr **an**
fr **u**
fr **i**
fr **t**

frog

fridge

fruit

idge
og
uit

fr____

fr_____

fr___

Stick the stickers to finish the pictures.
Read the words. Circle True or False.

It rained on Monday.
The builder liked it.

True   (False)

It rained on Wednesday.
The farmer didn't like it.

True   False

It rained on Friday.
The camper liked it.

True   False

It rained on Sunday.
The ducks loved it!

True   False

198

Write the words. Say the sentences.

It rained
on Thursday.

The painter
didn't like it.

The gardener
didn't like it.

It rained
on Saturday.

199

Play the game.

Sunday	Monday	Tuesday	Wednesday	Thursday	Friday	Saturday
	1	2	3	4	5	6
7	8	9	10	11	12	13
14	15	16	17	18	19	20
21	22	23	24	25	26	27
28	29	30	31			

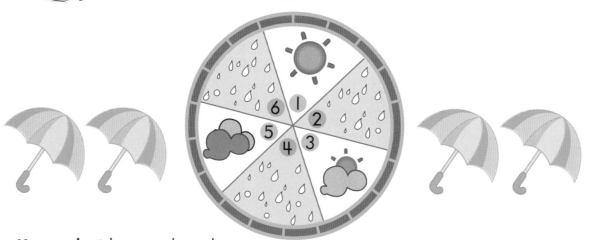

You need: stickers, number cube

1. Decide who goes first. Choose the color of your umbrella and collect the color stickers.
2. Throw the number cube. If you get a number that shows rain in the weather circle, say, "It rained on ___."
3. Put the umbrella sticker on the correct day and date.
4. If you get a number that shows a cloudy or sunny day, you can't use a sticker. (You wouldn't need an umbrella!)
5. The player who uses up their umbrella stickers first is the winner.

200

Write the words. Say the sentences.
Stick the stickers.

It rained on Monday.
The builder didn't like it.

It rained on Sunday.
The ducks liked it!

201

Sticker Sheet 20

Look at the picture clues.
Find and circle the words.
Write the words in the boxes.
Say the words.

a	v	q	s	i	f	h
g	m	e	k	x	r	n
o	f	r	o	g	i	c
c	p	e	r	s	d	a
f	r	u	i	t	g	w
e	o	g	v	s	e	y

 →

 →

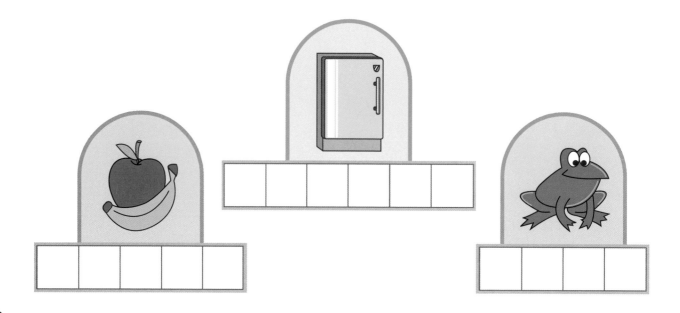

Trucks

Read *Trucks*. What do the trucks say?
Stick the stickers. Say the words in the speech bubbles.

I'm a ⬚ truck.

I'm a ⬚ truck.

I'm a ⬚ truck.

I'm a ⬚ truck.

I'm a ⬚ truck.

I'm a ⬚ truck.

Drive the trucks through the maze.
Stick the stickers to finish the words.
Stick the stickers that match.

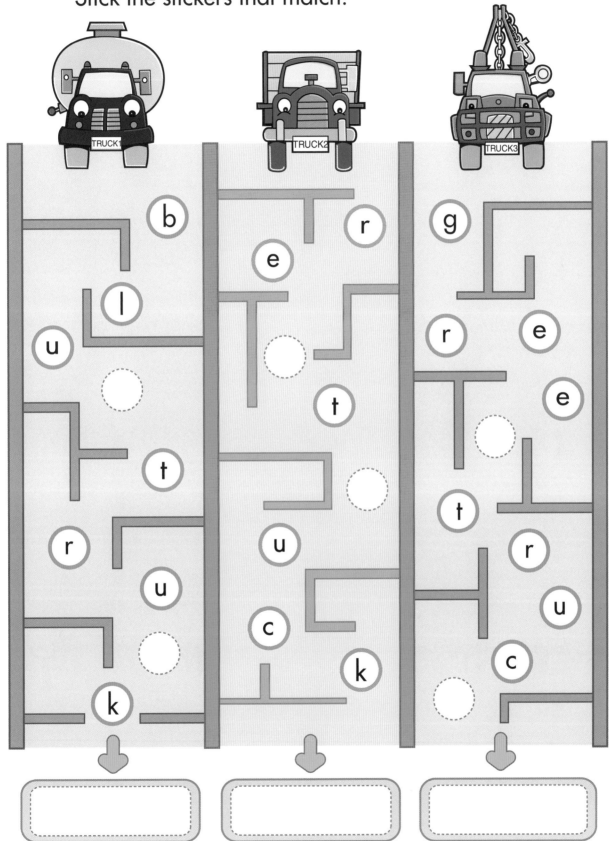

Sticker Sheet 21

Stick the stickers to make **tr-**.
Write the letters to finish the words.
Say the words.

truck

tractor

tree

train

Write the words. Stick the stickers.
Say the sentences.

w i t h

Zina is with a snake.

Zina is with a gorilla.

Zina is with a kangaroo.

207

Read the words. Stick the stickers to make a picture. Say the words.

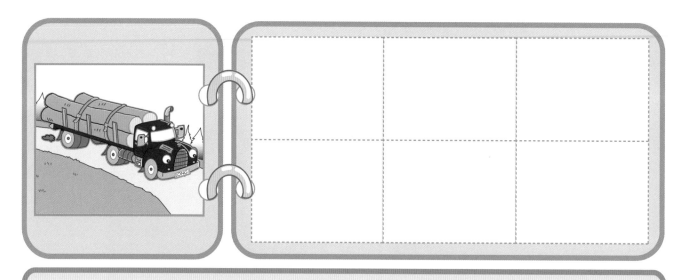

The blue truck said,
"I'm going down the road with a heavy load.
I'm a **long** truck."

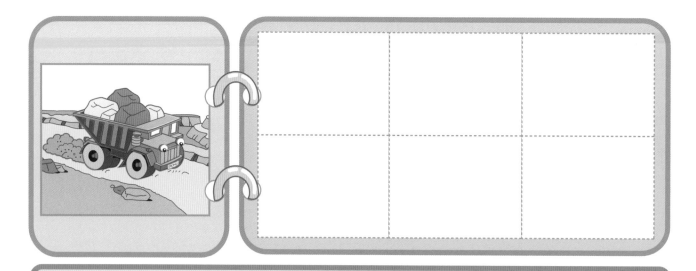

The green truck said,
"I'm going down the road with a heavy load.
I'm a **strong** truck."

Look at the picture clues.
Find and circle the words on the back of the truck.
Write the words in the boxes.

Play the game.

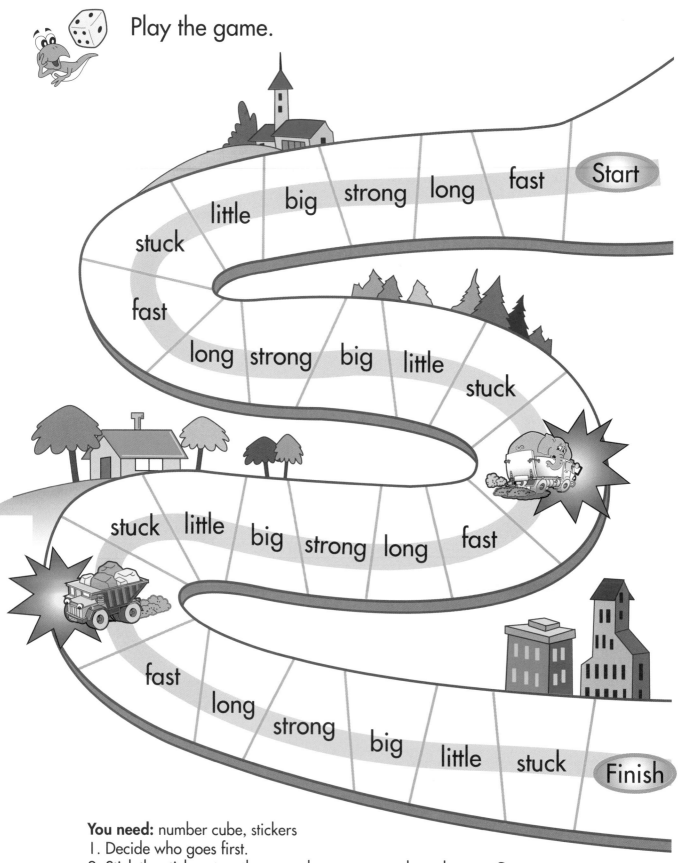

You need: number cube, stickers

1. Decide who goes first.
2. Stick the stickers together to make counters and put them on **Start.**
3. Throw the number cube and move your number.
   Say, "I'm going down the road. I'm a _____ truck", using the word that you land on.
4. If you land on a truck, go back to **Start.**
5. The player who reaches **Finish** first is the winner.

210

What is on the trucks? Write the words.
Fold the page on the dotted line.
Color the trucks to match the words.

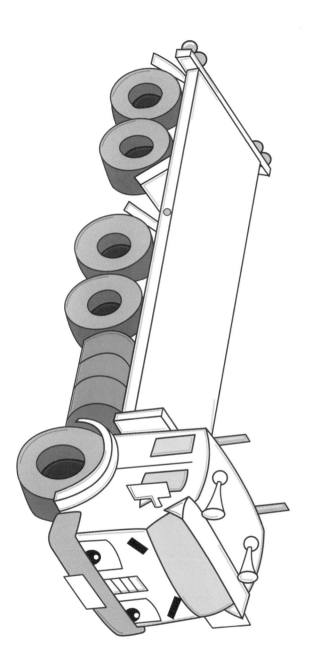

The orange truck

The red truck has a load of cars.

What is on the trucks? Write the words.
Fold the page on the dotted line.
Color the trucks to match the words.

The orange truck has a load of bananas.

The red truck

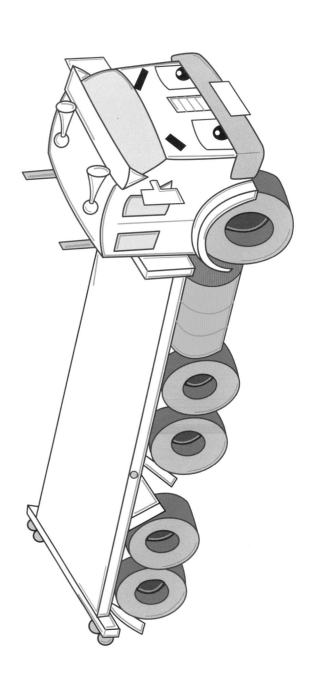

212

Sticker Sheet 1

Sticker Sheet 2

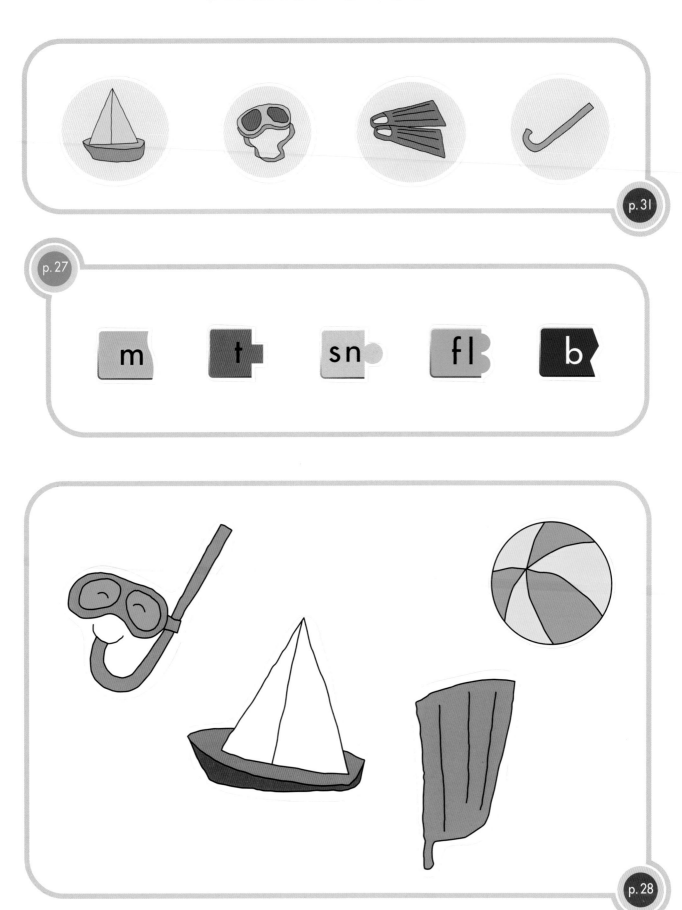

p. 31

p. 27

m   t   sn   fl   b

p. 28

Sticker Sheet 3

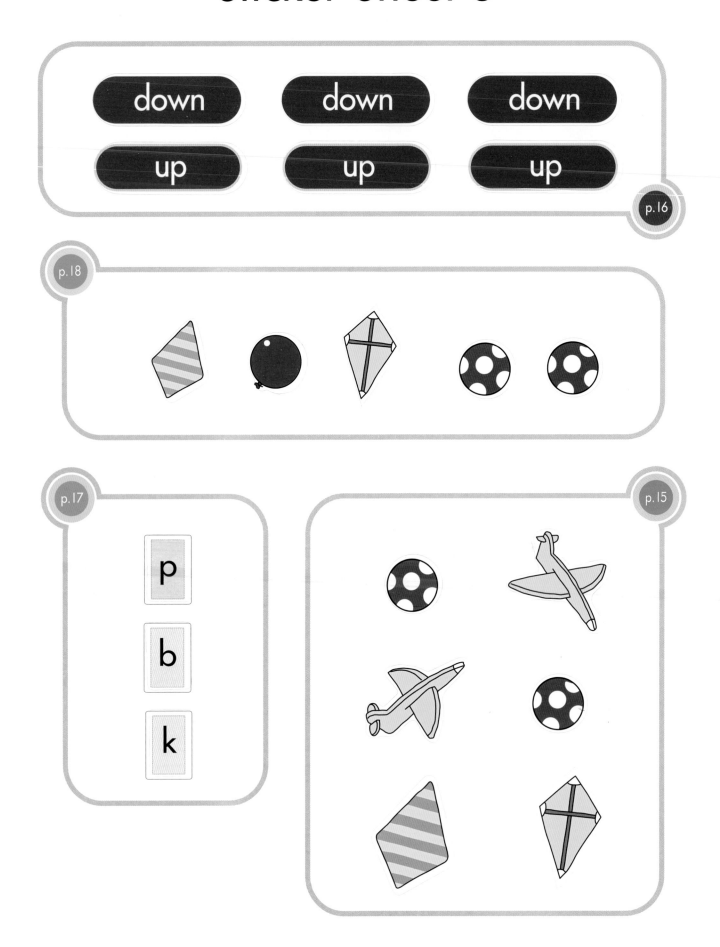

down   down   down

up   up   up

p.16

p.18

p.17

p.15

p

b

k

Sticker Sheet 4

p. 40

p. 50

p. 47

p. 41

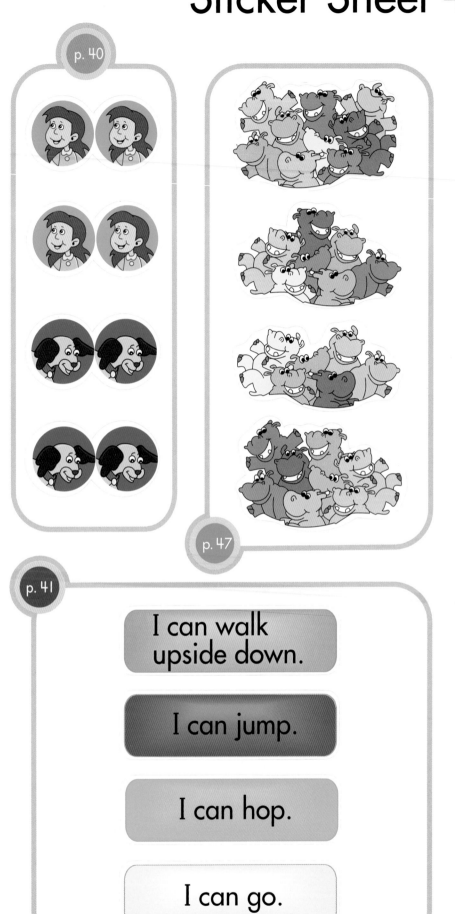

I can walk upside down.

I can jump.

I can hop.

I can go.

Sticker Sheet 5

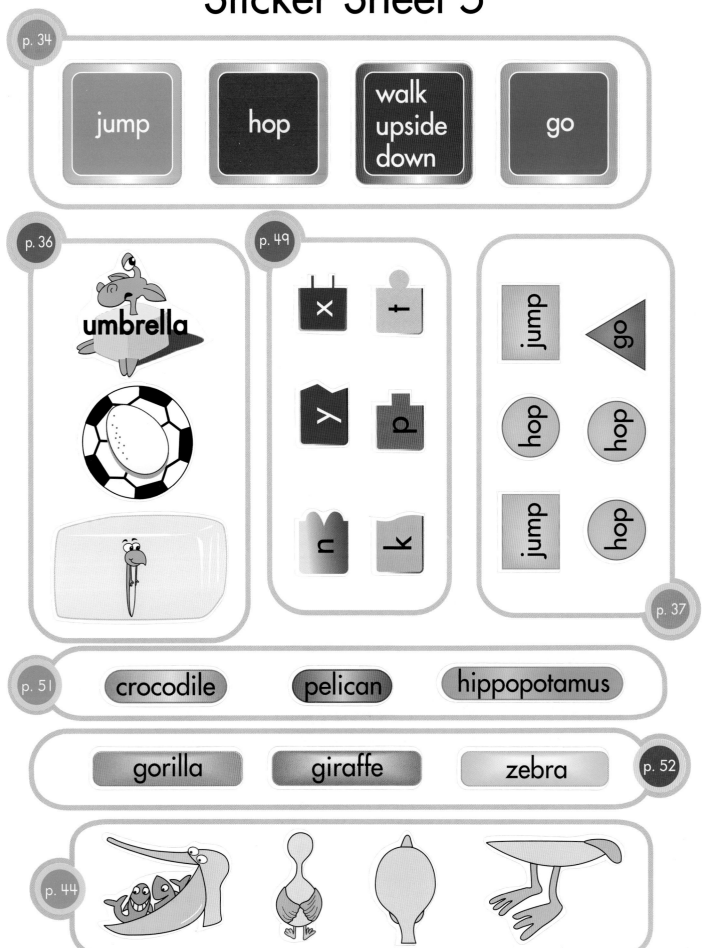

p. 34

jump

hop

walk upside down

go

p. 36

umbrella

p. 49

x

t

y

p

u

k

p. 37

jump

go

hop

hop

jump

hop

p. 51

crocodile

pelican

hippopotamus

p. 52

gorilla

giraffe

zebra

p. 44

Sticker Sheet 6

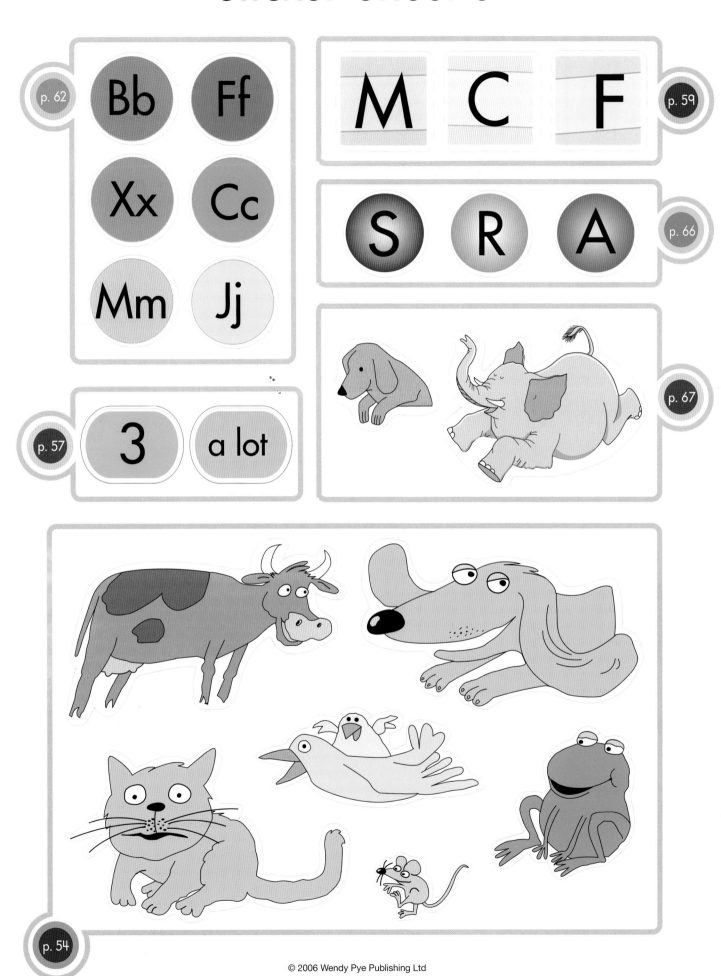

Sticker Sheet 7

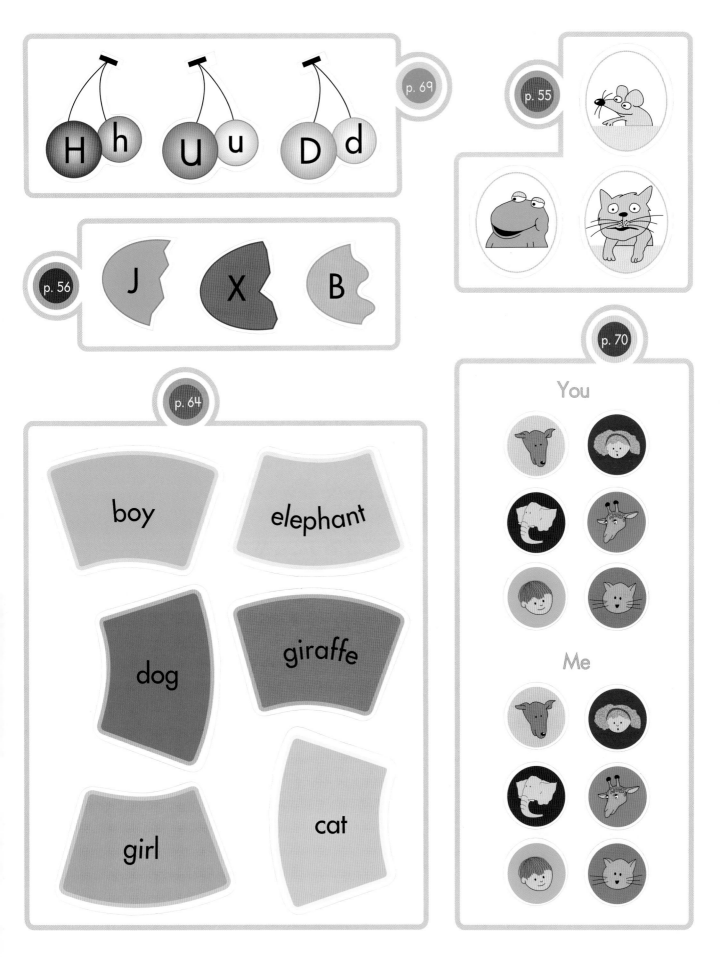

Sticker Sheet 8

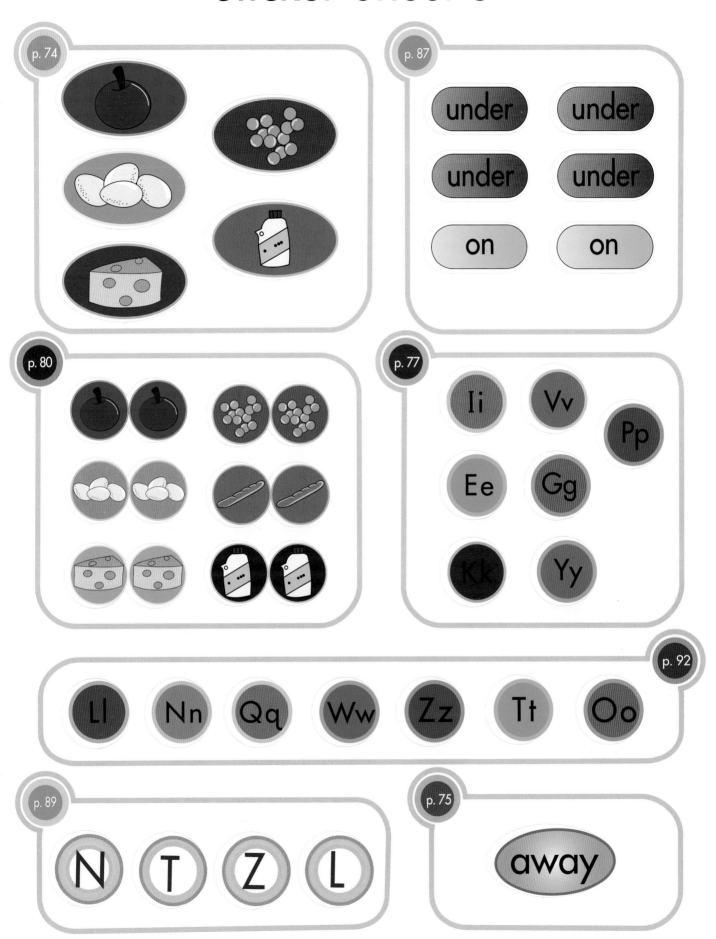

p. 74

p. 87

under under
under under
on on

p. 80

p. 77

Ii Vv Pp
Ee Gg
Kk Yy

p. 92

Ll Nn Qq Ww Zz Tt Oo

p. 89

N T Z L

p. 75

away

Sticker Sheet 9

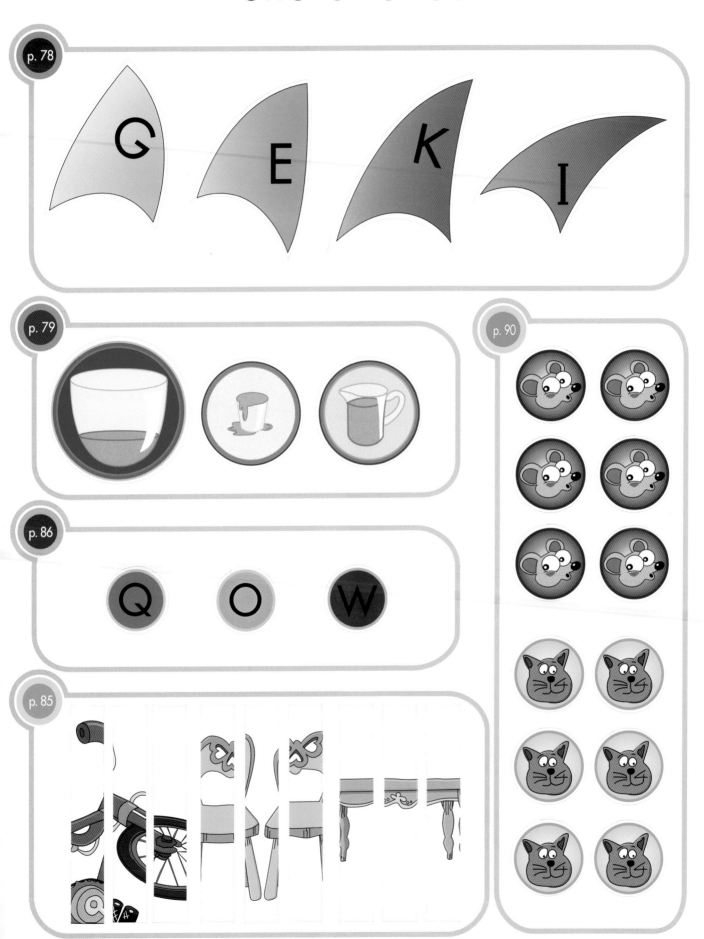

p. 78

p. 79

p. 86

p. 85

p. 90

Sticker Sheet 10

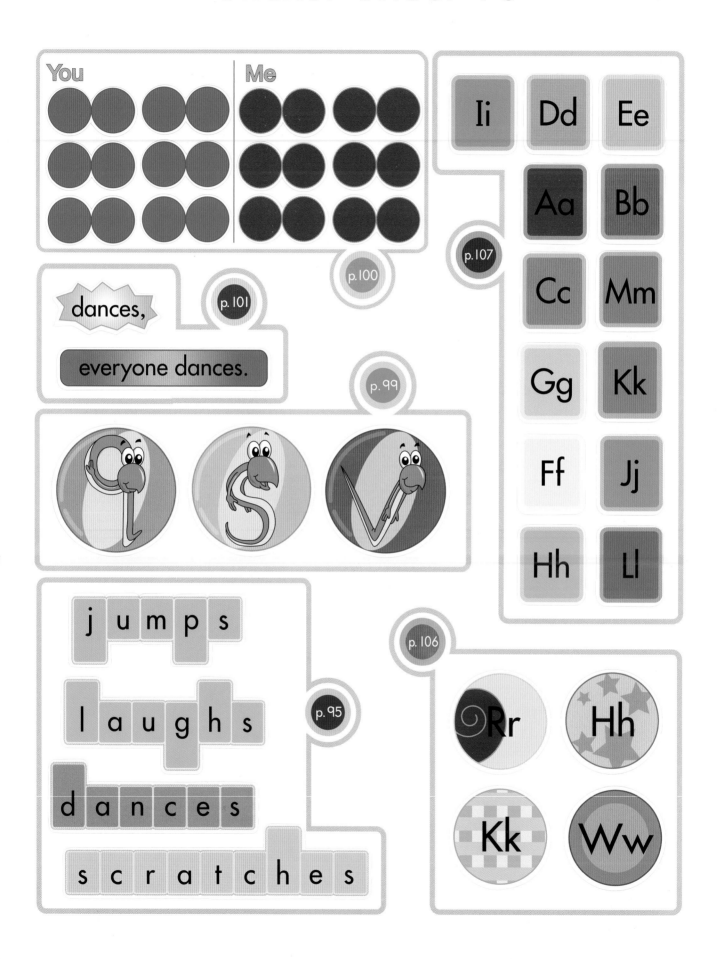

Sticker Sheet 11

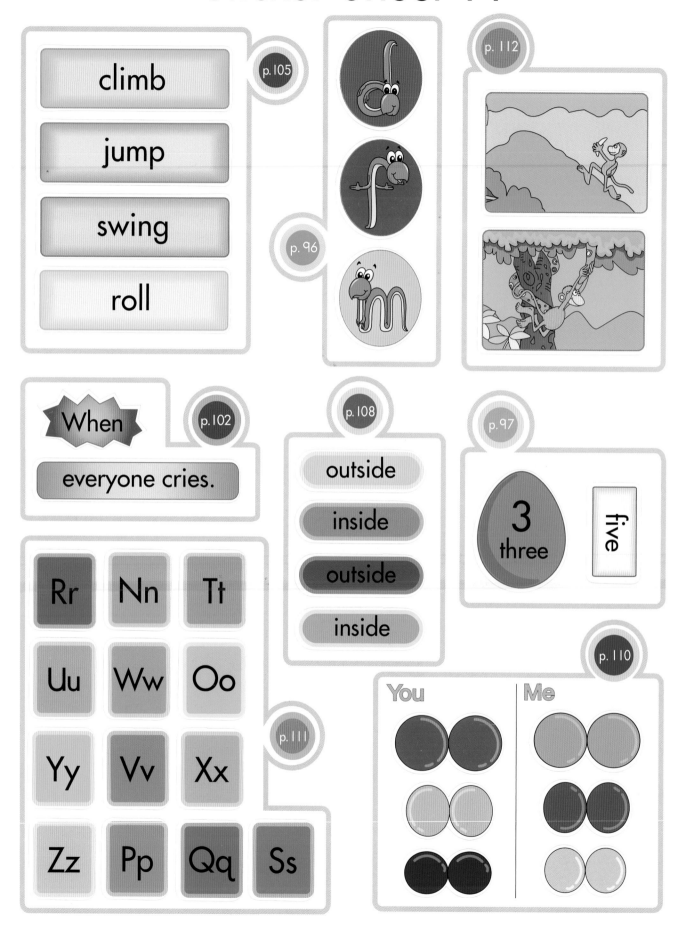

climb

jump

swing

roll

p.105

p.96

p.112

When

everyone cries.

p.102

outside

inside

outside

inside

p.108

p.97

3
three

five

Rr Nn Tt

Uu Ww Oo

Yy Vv Xx

Zz Pp Qq Ss

p.111

You   Me

p.110

Sticker Sheet 12

p. 114

donkey bee

monkey rat

frog cat

p. 115

cat

rat

frog

dog

p. 121

I will hide in here.

p. 117

p. 116

p. 127

but

but

a t

Sticker Sheet 13

Sticker Sheet 14

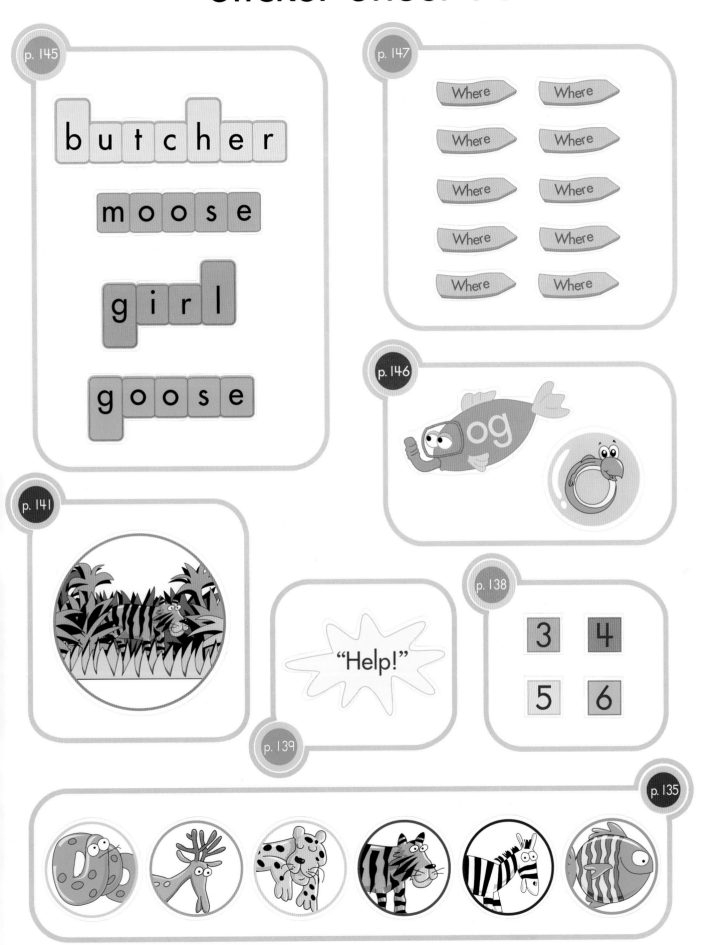

Sticker Sheet 15

p. 151

p. 136

p. 148

p. 150

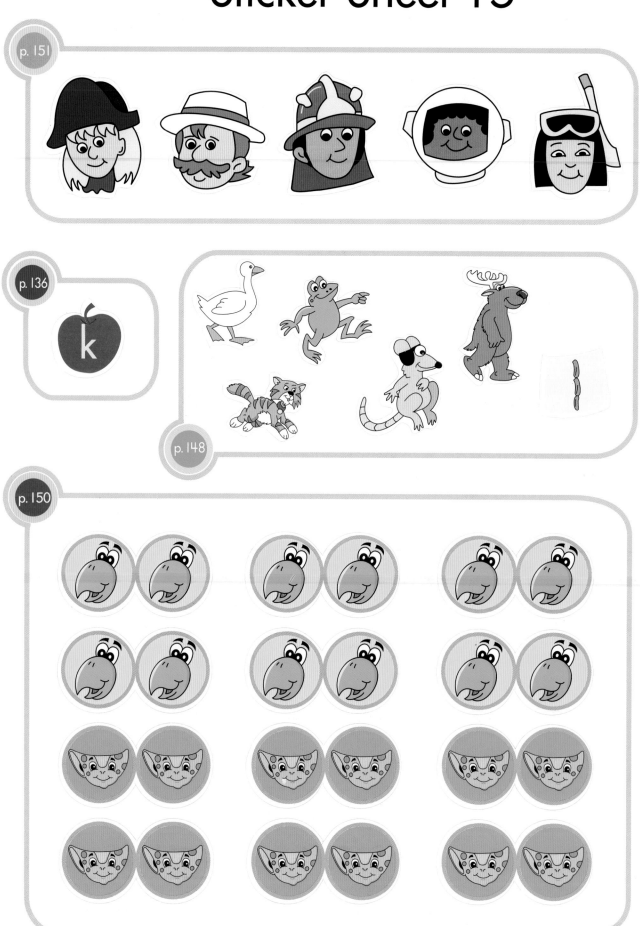

Sticker Sheet 16

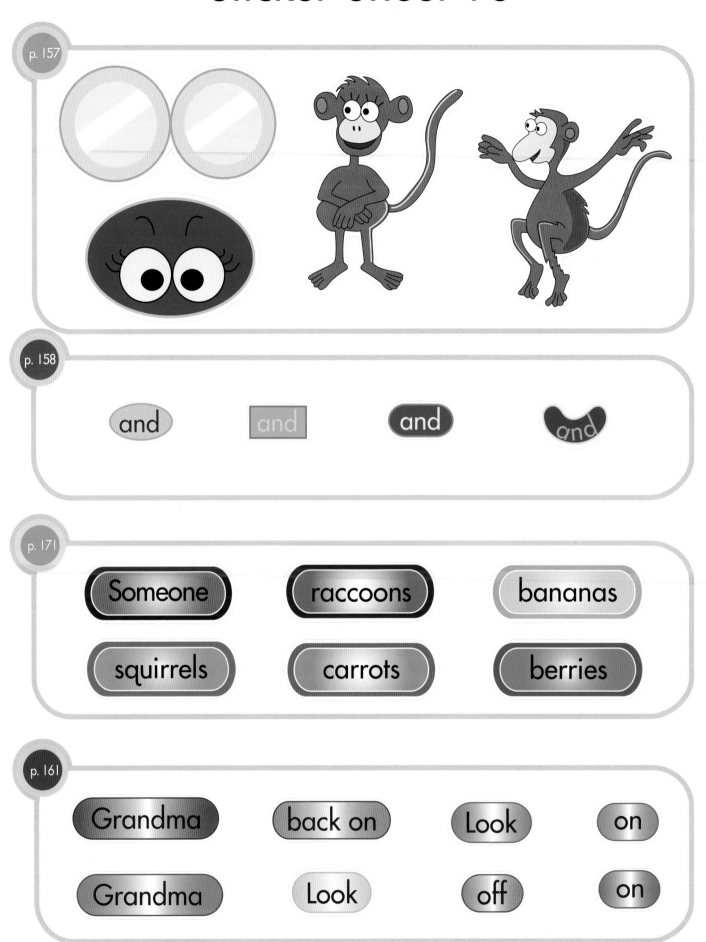

p. 157

p. 158

and   and   and   and

p. 171

Someone   raccoons   bananas

squirrels   carrots   berries

p. 161

Grandma   back on   Look   on

Grandma   Look   off   on

Sticker Sheet 17

p 164

food

p. 166

ate

p. 167

my

our

p. 154

And

And

p. 156

and

d

Sticker Sheet 18

rabbit

hippo

p. 181

p. 174

mother dog

little puppy

p. 185

p. 177

Sticker Sheet 19

p. 188

p. 186

ight

p. 176

ack

c

Muffin Cook Book

p. 184

p. 191

ice   cream   made

Mrs.   made

McGuire   some

sausages   .

p. 179

No one wants me.

I want the black one.

Sticker Sheet 20

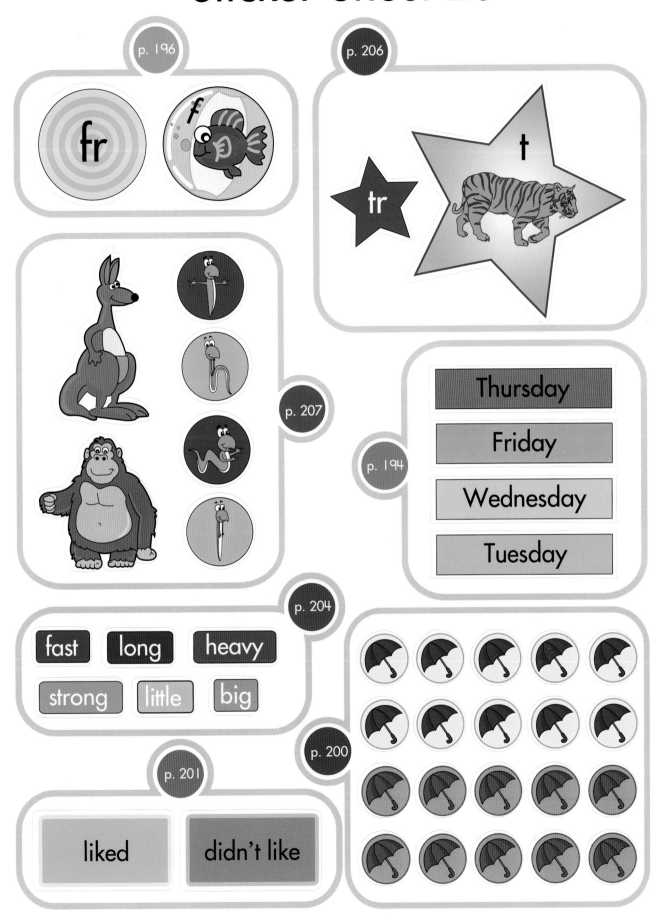

p. 196

p. 206

fr

f

t

tr

p. 207

Thursday

Friday

Wednesday

Tuesday

p. 194

p. 204

fast   long   heavy

strong   little   big

p. 200

p. 201

liked   didn't like

Sticker Sheet 21

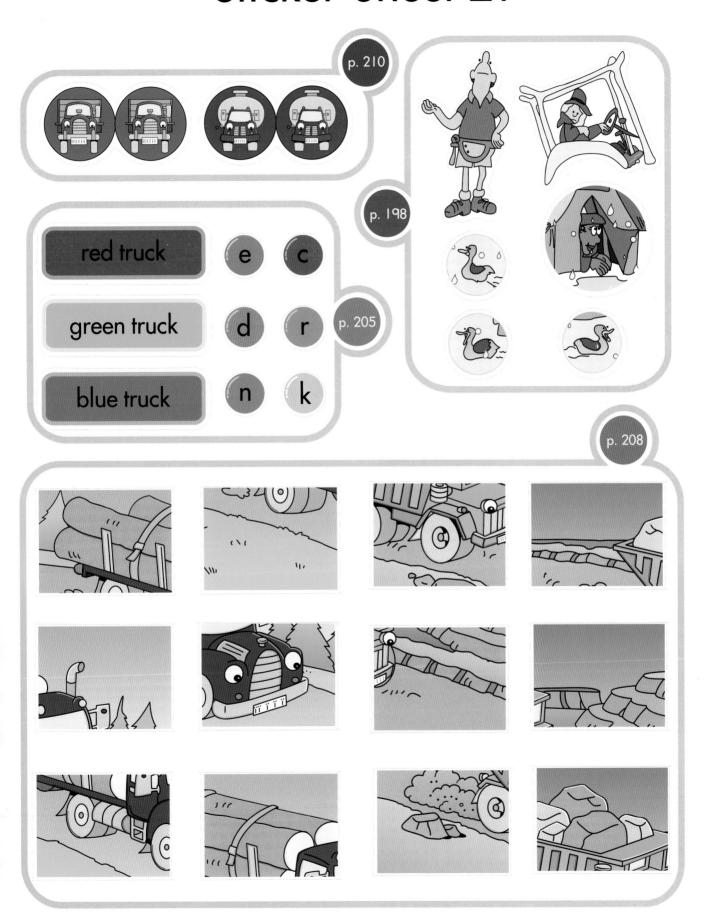

p. 210

p. 198

red truck   e   c

green truck   d   r   p. 205

blue truck   n   k

p. 208

Contents